LOVE WAR[...]

THE CONSCIOUS EXPERT'S GUIDE TO HEALING, JOY, AND MANIFESTATION

LAURA DI FRANCO

FEATURING: MILAGROS RUIZ BELLO, EDDIE BENABRAHAM, ROSALIND BERESFORD, DAN GORBUNOW, JESSICA HARVEY, DR. MAKEBA MORGAN HILL, SHARON JOSEF, ROCHEL MARIE LAWSON, BIRGIT LUEDERS, ABBIE MARTIN, MAUREEN MAYS, CAROLYN MCGEE, ANGELA ORORA MEDWAY-SMITH, DONNA O'TOOLE, GINNY ROBERTSON, ANGEL ROHRER, KYE SUN ROSE, LORI SAITZ, KATIE SHANLEY, PHIL TAVOLACCI

LOVE WARRIORS

THE CONSCIOUS EXPERT'S GUIDE TO HEALING, JOY, AND MANIFESTATION

LAURA DI FRANCO

Featuring: Milagros Ruiz Bello, Eddie BenAbraham, Rosalind Beresford, Dan Gorbunow, Jessica Harvey, Dr. Makeba Morgan Hill, Sharon Josef, Rochel Marie Lawson, Birgit Lueders, Abbie Martin, Maureen Mays, Carolyn McGee, Angela Orora Medway-Smith, Donna O'Toole, Ginny Robertson, Angel Rohrer, Kye Sun Rose, Lori Saitz, Katie Shanley, Phil Tavolacci

Heart Burst © Jo Jayson 2010 www.jojayson.com
Paintings, Prints, Products to Inspire, Heal and Empower

Free writing and business resources for Brave Healers
can be found at: https://lauradifranco.com/resources-vault/

DEDICATION

*For Shirley. Your courage lit my purpose on fire—
a fire that burns with just as much heat
as it started with, even seven years later.
Thank you for reaching out to me that day. I love you.*

DISCLAIMER

This book offers health and nutritional information and is designed for educational purposes only. You should not rely on this information as a substitute for, nor does it replace professional medical advice, diagnosis, or treatment. If you have any concerns or questions about your mental, physical, or emotional health, you should always consult with a physician or other healthcare professional. Do not disregard, avoid, or delay obtaining medical or health related advice from your healthcare professional because of something you may have read here. The use of any information provided in this book is solely at your own risk.

Developments in medical research may impact the health, fitness, and nutritional advice that appears here. No assurances can be given that the information contained in this book will always include the most relevant findings or developments with respect to the particular material.

Having said all that, know that the experts here have shared their tools, practices, and knowledge with you with a sincere and generous intent to assist you on your health and wellness journey. Please contact them with any questions you may have about the techniques or information they provided. They will be happy to assist you further!

TABLE OF CONTENTS

LETTER TO READERS ABOUT THE HEALING CRISIS

The healing crisis is a phenomenon that occurs on the healing journey. It's a form of awareness that is great to understand as you dive into these chapters. A healing crisis occurs when we feel the energy of an old wound, injury, or trauma as it's coming up to be released or healed. The resistance comes up in the form of thoughts, sensations, feelings, emotions, memories, and sometimes pain. These experiences often feel exactly like those you felt when the insult occurred.

Notice your reactions to them.

Sometimes it's exactly what you have the most resistance around (words, ideas, practices, conversations, events, etc.) that are the biggest opportunity for healing. Skilled healers recognize this and assist their clients through it with tools such as dialoguing, energy work, hands-on practices or modalities, and mindset or awareness coaching, among others.

The healing crisis, and your own resistance, are each an opportunity to go a layer deeper. They are doors to release and relief—to healing.

The problem, sometimes, is that when one is in the middle of a healing crisis, it feels like you're going to die, meaning the sensations, feelings, and emotions that surface can be that intense. The healers in this book get it. And we're here for you.

If you purchased this book (or it was gifted to you), you have access to a very special private Facebook group where our author experts are hanging out to assist readers with questions, support, or to take the conversation further. This is an incredible benefit to owning this book. You're not alone.

We're here to help you. Your questions will be welcomed and your concerns honored. You'll enjoy a safe space to continue your work of healing, and a community that has your back.

Get access to The Brave Healer Book Club on Facebook here: https://www.facebook.com/groups/143744423674578

See you there!

INTRODUCTION

"What is *Love Warriors* all about?" A healer friend asked this after seeing a post I made on Facebook.

"Love warriors show up in the world knowing their vulnerability is their strength. They consciously move into the sacred spaces of their lives choosing the higher vibrations of love, gratitude, joy, healing, compassion, courage, and kindness."

"I would be perfect for that!"

I smiled over the next few days as all my love warriors showed up, raised their hands, and joined me on this journey.

When I asked, "Who are my love warriors?" the authors in this book called themselves out with passion. They're people who fit the definition and want to write and share about it publicly. They want to help change the world with brave words. They are badasses. I love being around them.

Thanks to all of you—those who raised your hand for this project and those reading it. The fact you're here means you're part of this world-changing energy. That's exciting to me. You recognize that you *are* love.

You Are Love
By Laura Di Franco

If life has smothered your love
remember
love can't die
love has no kryptonite
the heart-soul-fire
of your love
whether raging or barely glowing
is still white hot
with a never-ending sweet breath
always blowing gently from underneath
silently stoking
helping you remember.
No matter how lost you become
how fearful
or helpless you feel
love is there
waiting patiently as your foundation
solid awareness.

You don't just stand upon it
you're breathing it.
It is you.
So if you feel the floor being ripped away
remember
you have wings
and love is the master teacher.
Let life try to take what you know

let go
surrender
love can't die.

When you fall and shatter
the mosaic of that heart-soul-fire
is not only more beautiful than before
she's brighter
more spectacular
more powerful
sparkling with an other-world flare.

She stands
with a wing span
greater than this lifetime.

Remember
love can't die
you are love
and you are a warrior.

Since 2016, I've told a story about one particular love warrior—Shirley. She's a bright spark who ignited my purpose simply by courageously reaching out to let me know she'd been helped by words in a blog I wrote. "Do you have any other links for me to read? I've been struggling. I'm a mother of five and have been feeling depressed." That message changed my life.

My dear Shirley, this book is dedicated to you and everyone seeking something more out of life and wanting to feel connected to something bigger. Since meeting you, I've built a community of people who care, a community of healers and world changers who walk their walk of awareness and love every day. Because you were brave enough to reach out, I embraced a chunk of missing worthiness I'd been searching for for a lifetime. Because you decided not to give up, I wake up on my worst days without entertaining giving up as an option. Because of you, I look at my fear of not-good-enough and say, "That's boring. What if your story could change (or save) someone's life? It's time to be brave."

Every single time I give myself that pep talk, I think of you. And I flip my switch to something more healthy, aligned, and badass. In my worst moments, I'm able to turn my face toward the sun, almost instantly recognizing that with awareness, I get a choice. I vowed to make that awareness my way of life and spread it as wide and far as possible for as long as possible.

I choose love now, every time, as fast as I can. Being a love warrior means reveling in the pause after feeling the sharp stab of heartbreak, betrayal, pain, or despair, and taking the deepest, juiciest, most full breath of gratitude. It means responding differently, breaking life-long conditioned habits of blame. It means feeling everything, and knowing the moment, as I practice full presence, allows me to radiate a light so bright that others instantly feel better.

Love warriors possess a sacred power used for good. They up-leveled their practice to a discipline of indomitable spirit and perseverance. They moved beyond their boring purpose-driven fears and chose to write, speak, and act in the name of love and divine justice.

I'm so honored to be here with these authors (and the entire community) doing this together. We're a revolution of brave healers addressing the old, outdated, unhelpful, harmful, toxic patterns we've been taught and breaking through to adopt new, healthy, helpful, aligned, aware means of being in the world.

When the idea of *Love Warriors* was conceived I sat in the middle of a multi-year battle with my daughter's abuser, faced with a very loud and excruciating wake-up call.

"He doesn't know who he's messing with," I told my friend. "Ever since this started, I've known my daughter and I were born to deal with this. Ever since this started, I've known something much bigger was at stake, that we're doing this for every girl who can't."

My definition of a love warrior changed while I experienced these events. They gifted me new levels of awareness about myself, my family, and people who abuse others. The situation challenged me to step up to face fear in new ways and to express opinions not generally shared by others. Love stepped out in front of me, purposefully getting in my way and in my face, and asked, "Can you be your true self now? And. . . how about now?"

I don't know, I thought at first.

I'm not sure I can do this.

I questioned everything, again, after 30-some years as a healer and 20-plus as a parent. I questioned my capacity to take on one more horrible thing, and my ability to be any kind of okay mother.

What if it's your fault?

Why didn't you see what was happening?

"It's just when we think we've done the work that the Universe tends to chuckle and give us something else to take us deeper."

I remember this conversation with a good healer friend.

"Yeah, and you look up and say, 'I thought I dealt with this already!'"

But there's always another layer, isn't there, brave healers? Sorry to tell you, my dear love warriors, this is part of what we signed up for. A lifelong healing journey means there is no destination of perfection or mastery. It means we chose to be teachers, and we're doing the work until we die. Then, maybe, doing it again in the next life if we must.

By the way, I'm convinced I had at least one past life as a cowgirl and another as a race car driver. Either that or my ancestors passed down some pretty crazy I-feel-the-need-for-speed genes. Anyone else love *Speed Racer* during those Saturday morning cartoons?

Whatever the challenge or purpose, I accept.

Whether I think I've dealt with it already, the Universe has other plans, or she's testing me so I can level up, I accept.

With a team of love warriors by my side, I accept.

I am not alone. I'm not giving up. I'm here with absolute faith in what I was born for. And I accept the challenge.

Whatever is thrown our way moving forward, I accept the challenge to show up, speak up, and love as hard and as much as possible. That includes loving myself, completely and radically.

This girl is a love warrior.

She's here to change the world.

And so are each of the authors in this book.

We're ready to help you practice the awareness, transform the pain, discover your purpose, and guide you to the healing, joy, and manifestation of the life you dream about. You're in capable, brave, skilled, and loving hands.

Grab hold, and let's walk together.

CHAPTER 1

YOU ARE A LOVE WARRIOR
HOW TO SHARE YOUR BRAVE WORDS AND CHANGE THE WORLD

Laura Di Franco, MPT, Publisher

This chapter and the poem called *This Girl* are dedicated to my daughter, the soul who truly taught me what 'brave' means. Standing by your side, Sweet Pea, has meant I had to stand taller than before and face all my demons. It meant I had to get to know myself even more and be willing to face the darker shadows. It meant truly understanding what matters to me and what I'm willing to fight for. I'm truly grateful you chose me as your mom and that you haven't given up on me. I'm still learning. I love you so much.

This Girl

By Laura Di Franco

This girl. . .

. . . knows her limits,

and won't make you guess.

She's sexy—dressed to impress—herself.

She'll say things that make you cringe,

because you were taught

that a girl shouldn't think of herself as a goddess.

You might try to make her see the error of her ways
but she redefined "error" a long time ago.
She's not falling for that show.

This girl. . .
. . . constantly stands in her power,
doesn't shy away from the fight,
will ask you to talk it out
if it's not making sense.

And you better watch the two cents you offer
because she knows what she's made of,
and that is priceless.

Her worth isn't defined by your limiting beliefs.

Her worth wasn't shattered by outdated, unhealthy ideas
of what a girl should be
or do
or become
or say.

She heard your argument,
and said WTF?
She questioned every bit
of the sideways, crazy-making shit
and had none of it.

She made her own rules instead.
With awareness,
compassion,
kindness,
and love,
she walked her walk through the world.

This girl...
... is the change.

This girl fights for every girl.

This girl speaks for every girl.

This girl heals for every girl who couldn't.

It doesn't matter how many times you knock her down.

When she's on her knees, she has already elevated her mind...
... the kind of mastery it takes 100 lifetimes to find.

And she just gets up—
no question about whether that's an option or not—
and stands tall, tears and all,
to go at it again.

She'll show you the private parts
of her heart
because she knows being exposed like that
is her strength.

And no weapon, word, or injustice
wielded in her direction
could ever come close to making a dent,
not in that beautiful, vulnerable, fantastic spark of soul
she was asked to show up to be.

When she answered her call
this girl stepped up immediately.

No hesitation.
No practice.
No warm-up.
No fear.

She raised her hand
and said, "I am love. I can do anything."

This girl. . .
. . . lit the world on fire.

MY STORY

When I started sharing brave words with the world in my blogs and books in 2008, they weren't really brave. I thought they were, but they were at a beginning level of 'brave.' They weren't at 'full-on brave' levels at first. I was too afraid of what others would think. That fear was still paralyzing me then.

We all start somewhere on this journey. We start where we are, with what we have, and we take some kind of action from that place. At least, if you want to go anywhere in life, that's what you should be doing.

I know now that we don't feel courageous, clear, and confident, first. If you're waiting to feel that way before you take action, good luck. You may never arrive at the place of your deepest desires if you're waiting to feel clear, confident, or brave enough before you begin or make the move. It's making the move that helps you feel that way. Go on, make the move, and then watch as the clarity, courage, and confidence arrives in the center of your chest, and you take a deep breath and say, "Whoa, I'm doing this! I can do this! I got this!"

The alternative is letting the fear paralyze you. I did that for a really long time.

This story isn't that story. You've read that one in my previous books already. *Living, Healing, and Tae Kwon Do*, and *Brave Healing* were the first brave words I shared with the world about being paralyzed and then changing my life. This story is different. It's about giving myself permission to feel the anger and consciously choose alignment with something that would actually help, rather than hurt, my life.

"I want to fight this."

I knew before my daughter said those words. I didn't know what 'fighting this' truly meant when I replied, "Okay," but I was on board, no matter what.

I knew I chose to be here, doing this work, in this lifetime, for this moment. I knew it without any doubt. What I doubted was my ability to survive the anxiety, fear, and cyclical, torturous, ruminating self-sabotage that would ensue as a result of saying yes to the fight.

OMG, I'm fighting myself right now.

"Laura Di Franco?"

"Yes, that's me."

"I'm sorry," the fully-outfitted police officer standing on my doorstep said as he handed me the subpoena, and I eyed the gun on his belt.

"Thanks," I replied and closed the door before he turned to walk away.

Nobody in my immediate family had ever received a subpoena before that day. Unfortunately, I answered the door at least seven more times over the almost three years of court battles, COVID delays, and postponements. I think waiting is worse than doing.

When we had (one of) our days in court, I looked around the room attempting to do a gut check on myself.

Nobody else is nervous. Isn't anyone else terrified?

"Are you okay?" I kept asking my daughter. "Do you need anything?"

"I'm good, Mom. No."

My gut churned in knots. The pressure in my chest was such that I imagined falling to the floor and the paramedics having to cart me away.

No! Stop that! You know how powerful your thoughts and words are. Stop that nonsense and just feel the feelings. Stop making them mean anything. You're okay. You'll be okay. Clear your mind. Get still. Relax.

I thought about every chapter of every book I've published since waking up on March 20, 2020 with the idea of doing a collaboration about healing. That's over 35 books, all offering generous, authentic stories of transformation and powerful self-healing tools. The book I was editing the week prior to our first trial was *Holistic Mental Health*.

Thank you, Universe. This is perfect timing.

And it always is, isn't it? The authors of that book didn't know it until now, but they helped me survive something, that as I paid attention to the visceral messages, I thought would kill me.

Breathe, Laura. Do your box breathing.

Inhale. . . one, two, three, four. Hold. . . one, two, three, four. Exhale. . . one, two, three, four. Hold. . . one, two, three, four. I repeated it five times.

Is that better? I don't know. OMG, they're going to find me passed out on the floor in here. My chest hurts.

I paced in a small room just outside the courtroom doors—a holding room for witnesses. I was alone. It was 12 feet by 12 feet with short grey carpet and a small wooden table with four matching chairs. Each witness was sequestered before (and after) their testimony, so they didn't talk to others about the case.

I'm going to die in here.

Maybe the feeling was of the unknown. This was my Saber-Toothed tiger. The feelings consumed me. My mind blared, choking me with nonsense, constant repetitive thoughts, trying to sort out the minutes that lay before me in any kind of way. There was no sorting this out ahead of time, though.

I turned toward one of the wooden chairs, placed my curled palms on the back edge, and started doing push-ups. "When you're really nervous before a talk, it helps to get physical," I remember a speaking coach saying. "Do some jumping jacks, or knee bends, or push-ups."

Is that better? Maybe a tiny bit. I don't know. OMG.

I closed my eyes and listened to the beat of my heart. I felt nauseous. There was a knock at the door, and an officer peeked in: "Ready for you."

I was escorted into the courtroom and through the swinging doors that separated the front of the room (judge, jury, attorney's tables) from the back (spectators). The officer pointed to the witness chair and motioned to the opening at the side where I could step into the wooden box and take my seat.

OMG, this looks like a coffin.

This *is* some kind of strange spectator sport, this trial thing. The warriors are in the arena, and they have coaches in their corners (attorneys). There's a main referee (judge) and helper referees (the jury).

It was my turn to speak. I had to be a warrior. I had to find my voice.

I sat in the black leather chair with my butt on the very edge, trying to adjust my mouth to the height of the microphone in my face. I reached into my pocket and rubbed my fingers over the edges of the black obsidian heart pendant my friend Stephanie gifted me a few months beforehand. "This is for protection," she told each of us, handing out the hearts as we sat in a circle, half high from the energy surge we all had after her breathwork session.

"Take something with you that you can hold and touch. You can use it to ground and center yourself and feel the energy of all of us around you. You're not alone."

"Thank you. It helps to imagine all of you with me," I told her.

As soon as the first question was asked, and as I spoke, I relaxed and felt blood rushing back into my shoulders. The waiting was much more difficult than the doing. I remembered my name and my address. I noticed my fingers were still cold. I answered each question to the best of my ability. It lasted about an hour, maybe a little more. I left the room, barely remembering what I said.

Was I even there?

I questioned my presence, this thing I spent a lifetime practicing. I wondered if the adrenaline high ruined my ability to say what I wanted to say. But it was over. I decided to be kind to myself and not question anything else for that day.

Deep breath, Laura. You're okay. You did it. You survived. Now it's time for you to help your daughter be strong.

I remember looking out into the audience during one of the very first open mic nights I performed at, shaking like a leaf. I remember my chaotic mind, trying to drown my precious presence, trying to steal the gift of the amazing moment from me. There were so many times I allowed that to happen, not realizing I have way more control than that—that it wasn't really about me at all.

It's not about you, Laura. It's about the thing you say that could help someone. It's about them. They want and need you to succeed. They need your confidence, your stellar performance. They need to be healed, and your fear is not helping.

When I remember it's not about me, I relax. The shaking calms. I feel my fingers and toes warm up. I actually smile. When I remember this is not about me anymore, and to relax into my body and allow something much bigger to run the show, things always feel good. It's the remembering that's tricky sometimes. It's remembering this while your body is in a full-on there's-a-Saber-Toothed-tiger-here mode that's tricky. Because when you feel like you're going to die, something very primal kicks in. It takes a ninja level of awareness to pause there, and choose to feel, do, be, and say something different.

No matter what you're going through, it's the awareness that gives you a choice. It pays to practice. And when you're attempting to feel brave enough to share your story in a bigger way, it's going to be the awareness, then the action, that helps you get to the 'brave.'

Let's practice, shall we?

THE PRACTICE

I know you want to share your brave words, too. You are a love warrior. Your message matters. What if the thing you're still a little afraid to share is exactly what someone needs to hear to change, or even save, their life? It's time to be brave.

There are levels of sharing I'm about to guide you through. Each level requires you to move past a certain amount of fear. Notice each one. Feel your body. Stay in there and notice. Feel grateful for being alive and the exquisite experiences you're having. Surrender. Stay down in your body with deep pelvic bowl breaths. Notice everything.

In his book, *The Surrender Experiment*, Michael Singer said about his intense experience in court: "I enjoyed spending my day letting go of whatever that voice in my head was trying to say and deeply relaxing whenever my heart began to feel anxious. In this situation, surrender was not an option, it was the only sane thing to do."

I want you to practice a little bit of surrender as you follow the steps to sharing your brave words, and changing the world.

What you need: A notebook and pen, and your body awareness practice.

The Love Warrior's Guide to Sharing Brave Words

Level 1—Journaling

Write to Feng Shui your soul:

Moving the words from inside your head to the outside—onto a piece of paper—is the first level of healing. When you write them down, you become your own witness. This is a powerful awareness practice. If you don't do any of the other steps here, do this one, and keep doing it. You'll learn life-changing things about yourself. And when you do that, you're already changing the world! One of the best coaches I've ever worked with started by giving me the homework of writing a page and a half every day, no matter what, no matter if I thought I had anything to write about or not. Thank you, Torrie.

Take out your notebook and with a deep breath, start to journal everything. Write as fast as you can without censoring yourself. Write every detail of the story. Don't leave anything out. You can choose to keep the writing, or burn it. One of the fears people have at this level is that someone is going to read the journal. It's not keeping the writing that matters. It's the movement of the writing which shifts the energy and clears a space inside you. Journaling is writing to Feng Shui your soul.

Level 2—Speaking out loud

Move the words from your heart to your tongue:

Putting the vibration of your voice to the words is the powerful next level of healing. When you hear your own words, spoken out loud to yourself, you'll create a witness at another deeper level.

Read what you wrote out loud to yourself. Take the time to journal a little bit about how that made you feel, or add any additional thoughts or aha moments afterward. When it's out loud, it's real. You'll feel this in your heart.

Level 3—Speaking out loud to a friend

When someone else acts as the witness, everything moves to the next level of healing. This is done with a trusted, beloved friend or person who knows how to hold a sacred healing space with active listening. Their only job is to listen to you read out loud.

Let your friend know you're not looking for any feedback or comments. Let them know their only job is to listen to you read. Read what you wrote out loud to your friend. Notice what you feel. Stay in your body and notice. Take the time to journal a little bit about how you felt reading to someone else, or any additional thoughts or a-ha moments afterward. If it feels right to discuss any of it with your friend, do that.

Level 4—Writing for others to read

Making the decision to write for someone else (a letter, blog, chapter, book, or anything else you're writing for someone else other than yourself) is the next level of healing. What can happen at this level is the inner critic shows up full force with all kinds of self-sabotaging thoughts about why your message isn't good, perfect, or unique enough. Your job is to write the piece with your person or people in mind and then ask someone (trusted) to read it and give you feedback.

After finishing the writing, send it to your friend or friends and ask for specific feedback. A great way to ask for feedback at first is, "What did you like most about this?" Or, "What places were your favorite, and why?" You'll either receive the feedback in writing, or in person. Either way, ground and center yourself with some deep pelvic bowl breaths, and keep yourself open to all feedback, realizing that everyone who reads your writing comes from a unique set of filters. In the end, we are our own worst critics. Notice what you feel after receiving the feedback. Take some time to reflect and journal about what you noticed, adding any thoughts or a-has.

Level 5—Speaking out loud to an audience

This step is a big one for most people who want to share their brave words. There's something about hearing your own voice reverberating against the walls in a room from the speakers. It's scary! And it takes practice grabbing the microphone and not feeling like your body will turn to Jell-O. But it's also one of the most deeply healing things you can do. Sharing your voice at a local open mic, on a small stage, or even in an online event will be a catapult to your audience getting to know, love, and trust you.

When you're brave and share out loud with an audience, get ready for your inner critic to run around screaming and crying in your head. Every time you level up, this can seem worse. Notice it. Stay in your body. Breathe. Learn from the experience.

Find a place you're able to share your story from the stage. Make a date and do it! Take some time to journal any thoughts, feelings, or a-has afterward. Surrender to the experience as part of your practice, and feel grateful for the opportunity!

Level 6—Publishing your writing

This one is last on my list because of the big feelings and aftermath I've watched authors move through after their book (or blog, post, or other writing) goes live online and they realize the entire world can read their words. The reality is, unless you're Stephen King (or insert the name of your favorite famous author), only a small part of your corner of the world is reading. But it can feel very scary to publish. The good news? You can start small and work up to big. You can publish a social media post, a blog, an article in a magazine, a chapter in a book, or a whole book.

The most common fears about publishing:

What if I change my mind?

Authors are afraid that what they're writing about now will change later, meaning they won't think the same things or their journey will take them to some sort of transformational moment, and they won't believe anything they wrote anymore. Answer? Write your next piece. It's okay to change your mind.

What if I upset or hurt someone I love?

What I know for sure about my love warriors is they don't have intentions of hurting anyone. Their priority is healing themselves. After the basic tips like, "Change any names or facts that compromise the identity of your subject," I often refer to my favorite writing quote of all time:

"You own everything that happened to you. Tell your stories. If they wanted you to write warmly about them, they should've behaved better."

Anne Lamott

What if someone disagrees, or worse, dislikes me?

This might be the absolute worst paralyzing fear of most writers. And when you play big in the world, it's not *if* the critics will show up, it's *when*. I'll never forget what my friend Phil said to me one day about his book: "Hey, Laura, look, I got a one-star review! You know you've made it when you get a one-star review."

Love ya, Phil. And, yes, you definitely know you're making waves when you begin to ruffle some feathers and attract a critic or two. I know I stand for something when this happens. I'm okay with that. It's not your job to make everyone like you. It's your job to like yourself. And the only way to like (or love) yourself is to *be* yourself. Don't write what you think other people want to read. Write what you love. Write about what matters to you. Write and speak about what you stand for.

Maybe you have more fears about publishing. I'd like to finish this chapter by saying, who's your Shirley? This is not about you anymore. It's about the person whose life you'll change, or even save, when you're brave enough to share your words.

It's time to be brave!

Laura Di Franco, MPT is the CEO of Brave Healer Productions, where they specialize in publishing and business strategy for healers. She spent 30 years in holistic physical therapy and 12 in private practice before making the pivot to publishing. With 14 years of training in the martial arts and 40 books and counting, including over three dozen Amazon bestsellers, she knows how to help you share your brave words in a way that builds your business and your dream life.

Her daily mission is to help fellow wellness practitioners do what they need to do to change the world in less time and with fewer mistakes and heartache on the journey. She shares her authentic journey, wisdom, and expertise with refreshing transparency and straightforward badassery. Hold on to your seat because riding alongside her means you'll be pushed into and beyond your comfort zone and have way more fun with your purpose-driven fears on a regular basis.

When Laura chills out, you'll find her with a mojito at a poetry event with friends, driving her Mustang, bouncing to the beat at a rave, or on a beach in Mexico with something made of dark chocolate in her mouth.

Connect with Laura:

https://LauraDiFranco.com

https://www.Facebook.com/BraveHealerbyLaura/

https://www.Instagram.com/BraveHealerProductions

https://www.Twitter.com/Brave_Healer

https://www.linkedin.com/in/laura-di-franco-mpt-1b037a5/

https://www.youtube.com/@bravehealerproductions2444

"Your fear of not-good-enough is boring. It's not about you anymore. Your words will change someone's life when you're brave enough to share them. It's time to be brave!"

– Laura Di Franco

CHAPTER 2

THE LOVE TRIANGLE OF THE SELF

UNLEASHING YOUR TRUE POWER THROUGH SELF LOVE AND BEYOND

Eddie BenAbraham

Lifetimes of gratitude to my wise and loving parents, Malka and David, my amazing brothers Isaac and Joe, and awe-inspiring Suns, Ariel and Eytanel. Love you, always.

MY STORY

Last year I received a message from them: *We are seven, and we are coming to teach you the secrets of the universe.*

The discovery of "Self" can be basic and focused on the obvious, or it can lead you into the depths of the divine intelligence of your soul.

We live on a planet that has been here far long before we arrived, and for that, she deserves our profound respect. Gaia is alive and aware in more ways than we give her credit for. She knows each and every one of us by name. She knows where you came from and the potentials you're preparing for your future. Your existence is a miraculous event that created you in the image of the One—Source, God, the ultimate Creator.

How do we define God? *Pure-love.*

Do we know what love is? Almost everyone I've met says they love. They love their parents, children, brothers, sisters, friends, dogs, and cats. But do we love everyone the same way or to the same degree? Is love quantifiable? And if so, who and how can love be measured?

If we can measure and quantify love, we then know love has substance. You can detect and measure it. Similarly, we can detect and measure light or sound.

As I stand here at the borderline of sand and water, by the salty waves of the Pacific Ocean, I look into the distant horizon where the clear blue sky is kissing the water as if they're one. There is no other place I'd rather be right now; I'm in bliss and calm, looking back in time, connecting the dots of the past leading to this moment. Everything that took place was precisely orchestrated by the divine Creator. If that's a fact for me, then your life must be similar with respect to divine timing and events. The so-called "challenges" are the ones that come to mind when you question your path. Although in reality, every challenge has a reason and the reason is—you.

I've spent more time at the beach in the last six months than I can remember. I was called to meet them here so we could work together. It's now July; Malibu Beach is hot but comfortable, in the lower eighties. I found this little isolated spot, and not many visit because parking spaces are limited. I often take my forty-minute drive here early in the morning during weekdays and find myself all alone standing with my feet in the water, breathing in the powerful ocean water.

That's when I received the message.

A few months passed, and it was slowly becoming clear that I must be here by the water. And then, about eight months later, on April 1, 2022, they finally revealed who they are:

We are the Seven Founders

The Original Whales.

It was a moment I'll never forget. Everything I went through was now understood. Starting from my childhood experiences and visions, moving to a new country in my teens, the people I met, the relationships, the books I read, the jobs I had and businesses I created, the challenges, struggles, pain, and, yes, the successes. But mostly the last 15 years, which I now call my "spiritual boot camp." All of it is now crystal clear; deep breath.

Your life journey isn't random; you're not here by mistake or created to live one lifetime and then be done. What if I told you you're so magnificent and powerful; everything you are today is because of one thing—Love.

This Love I speak of is the energy of God, Source, Divine Creator. Whichever way you choose to name the *absolute Love*, it is exactly that.

Every breath you take is divinely manifested by the laws of the Creator. These laws can be identified in different ways. For example: When you expand your chest, your body prepares your lungs to receive air created by the delicate balance of the flora on Earth. These systems support the trees to collaborate in the beautiful process of giving us the oxygen and water we need. If you look closely at this particular process, you'll witness that in each step, precise geometrical, mathematical, and energetic processes are visible to your awareness.

You are a masterpiece created by the wisdom of the greatest love there is.

When I left the beach that April morning, I didn't know that four weeks later, I'd experience another dramatic shift that would show me the new path I had to take.

It was another beautiful hot day; my home was clean, with newly-bought rugs for my little kitchen and bathroom. Laundry and dishes were done, and most importantly, my Suns, Ariel (15) and Eytanel (13) enjoyed the healthy lunch I made, and then it was time to take them to their mother's home. That day, I felt a deep need to go to the beach. My mind was a bit cluttered with the multitude of tasks I was managing at work that week, and yet still very focused. Just like previous times, as I was driving through the beautiful green canyon leading to Malibu Beach, the Whales showed me the subject we were about to work on. Compared to past channellings from other divine sources, the Seven Founders have a very distinct intensity in how they deliver messages. I'm sure I'll be able to identify each Whale at some point. Perhaps by learning their names first and then recognizing the style of the message delivered. We shall see. At this point, this connection is still fresh. *I must give it time to mature, just like any other friendship.* As soon as I arrived, I knew it would be like having my own private beach again. The thought still baffles me. *Los Angeles County is blessed with over twenty million residents, and yet I'm the only one at this beach this late in the afternoon?!*

The waves were fairly strong, but the weather was calm, with scattered fluffy white clouds that didn't bother the sun from shining on the little part of "my" beach. It was April 26th, and I had made a few audio recordings with the Whales by that time. The subjects were fascinating and, at the same time, familiar. Because since 2009, I've been receiving information about a particular esoteric system, one that took me years to understand and eventually work with.

What if I said you have an energetic system around you the size of a football field? Would you believe me? Well, you don't have to, but at least keep an open mind because it relates to our main subject of self-love.

I called this energetic field "The Soul's Mantle Grid" (In Hebrew:(סְרִיגֵי לִיבַּת הַנְשָׁמָה)). It was 2009 when I was first shown parts of it. It was vague, without colors yet. I was aware of the first set of Merkabahs (the energy mechanism associated with your soul's projection into the physical body) prior to this revelation, but this was not it because this one was much bigger. During the following three years, I was shown the basic construct of The Soul's Mantle Grid, and in 2011, I publicly shared the first sketch. Although it was clear in my vision, I knew this was not all of it and that I must be open to what I was guided towards.

At this point in my story, I wish to reveal the premise:

The more you become aware of your magnificence, the wider you are in your capacity to the love of Self.

When you become aware of your Soul's Mantle Grid, you learn about the magnificent being that you are. The anatomy of your soul is revealed with its capacity to ignite the flame of self-love and beyond.

The journey of self-love is always present. If one chooses to, he or she will unravel the layers of this profound transformation that has one objective—to step closer and closer to your divine self.

Through the journey of self-love, you heal yourself, consciously create your reality, and live in joy and bliss.

"Eddie, what do you mean by self-love? Isn't it selfish to love yourself and not think of others?"

Ha yes, the question I encounter most. No. It's not love for power or greed from a place of lack, control, and fear. Instead, It's pure and unconditional love.

With the following words, I'll demonstrate what self-love means to me. It's one most mothers have experienced. However, men have such capacity as well.

Let's go back in time to the day you were in labor. You're in the delivery room, ready to give birth to your child. The room is warm and cozy, and the nurses and staff attend to your every need, but the pain is growing, and the contractions are now closer and closer. Hours pass, and you're now in full labor, pushing with all your might. The tension is high, and the doctors raise their voices, guiding you to give one last big push.

You did it!

The pain is gone, and your child is breathing air and placed on your chest, skin to skin.

You stare into each other's eyes.

Now, I ask you, what is this powerful grand-love you're engulfed within every cell of your being?

This is the love of the Creator!

This is the closest we know of it. This is it! This is the type and level of love I want you to feel toward yourself every time you look in the mirror.

As a man and father, I can assure you that anyone can achieve the embodiment of self-love. The key is choice; when you choose to walk the journey of self-love, Source will guide you and provide you with unique lessons.

I always remember my father's eyes as he lovingly looked into mine. The first time my boys said, "Abba, I Love You." Mother Nature, with her unmeasurable magnificence loving me unconditionally.

Remember, free choice is the catalyst of life.

Imagine a triangle. At one point is self-healing, at the second is creating your reality, and at the third, joy and bliss. Now at the center of this triangle, add the primary ingredient holding those three together, making them possible—falling in love with yourself.

About forty minutes passed. The soothing sounds of the ocean waves were interrupted by the ring of my cell phone. I hesitated to look and answer because I was in my zone and didn't want any interruption. It was my dear next-door neighbor. I couldn't ignore this call. As soon as I said hello, his voice was loud and urgent:

"Eddie! Your house is on fire!"

"Where are you?"

It's been three months since that intense day. In the first few moments, I felt the shock overwhelming my thought process but quickly returned to clarity. There was nothing I could do at that moment. I calmly gathered my belongings from the sandy beach and walked toward my car.

Everything I owned was in that loving house, but I was not attached to anything. Trust is the state of being I chose to be in. *I hope no one was injured. How did the fire start? What is going on there now? I'll be there in 40 minutes. Will I be able to salvage anything?* So many thoughts could've fogged my intention at that point, but I knew it was time to simply let go.

By the time I arrived home, the Los Angeles fire department had done an incredible job. My amazing landlord and neighbors were happy and relieved to see me. My beloved brother Joe was already there; I called him first when I left the beach. About thirty minutes later, Ariel and Eytanel arrived. We hugged and looked at our charred home, then I looked into their eyes and said:

"Boys, this is a beautiful experience. It is time to move on to our next adventure. This is a new opportunity. Let's celebrate these moments."

Thankfully, no one was hurt, and all the important things I needed to continue my work, plus my entire closet, were saved.

The title of my chapter is:

"Unleashing Your True Power Through Self Love and Beyond."

What do I mean by "Beyond"?

What is waiting for us beyond our love of Self?

The answer is:

Falling In Love With Your Soul.

THE PRACTICE

THE ANATOMY OF YOUR SOUL - CONNECTING WITH YOUR SOUL'S MANTLE GRID

The objective is to discover your magnificence by learning your soul's anatomy.

To start this journey, you'll connect to your own Soul's Mantle Grid.

The Soul's Mantle Grid is the powerful system that melds your soul-piece into your physical expression (your physical body).

There are many so-called systems that are part of this grand game of life; for example, Earth is a system, astrology, reincarnation, Akashic records, the animal kingdom, etc.

Many generations ago, the secrets of the Soul's Mantle Grid were taken away from us. Now, it's back to help us expand our consciousness and help create Heaven on Earth.

This is a beautiful opportunity to become aware of your power and magnificence.

Awareness is key because when you become aware of something, you then have the choice to access its power and embodiment through your consciousness.

In this practice, I'm inviting you to push your skills to the max while being patient with yourself and the entire process of discovery.

When your soul is ready to incarnate into the physical body, it uses the Soul's Mantle Grid to divinely fuse into the physical aspect of yourself.

Where is the Soul's Mantle Grid?

All of the so-called human systems reside in the quantum and etheric realms, and some are in the physical realm as well. The Soul's Mantle Grid resides in all three realms: quantum, etheric, and physical.

The Soul's Mantle Grid is multidimensional, which makes it relatively challenging to see and understand.

What's in your Soul's Mantle Grid?

- Your body

- Aura

- Meridians

- Chakras

- Merkaba

- Torus

- Sphere-matrix

- Secondary Merkaba

- Upper and lower light-tubes

- Body-intelligence

- The six potential timelines

- God's timeline 7

- The Healing Consul "Hall" (The Healing Ambassadors)

- Ten Sefirot—emanations

- The twelve layers of DNA

- And more.

During your meditation, you'll focus your attention on one or more of the following "ingredients:"

- The Sphere-Matrix represents the entire oval-shaped field that is 369 feet wide and about 277 feet tall.

- Above and below are the funnels that cup the sphere matrix. The top funnel extends to Source, and the bottom, to Gaia's core.

- The secondary Merkabah is about sixty-seven feet wide and tall. There are six layers. Meaning six Merkabah occupying the same space.

- The torus extends around the first three sets of Merkabah that are about twenty-eight feet in length and height. Within this space are the aura, body-intelligence, meridians, chakras, the physical body, and more.

It's best to do this work outdoors. As you get better at it, I invite you to try anywhere else you like.

Choose a big open space like a local park, beach, or grassy playing field. Sit comfortably where you have at least two hundred feet around you with no interruptions—no trees, buildings, fences, or people present.

Begin with a grounding meditation of your choice. When done, bring your arms ninety degrees to your side with your palms open, facing forward. Keep your eyes closed, and say the following:

Dear Creator, thank you for showing me my Soul's Mantle Grid and teaching me its true essence, power, and majesty.

Keep your eyes closed and maintain your meditative state. While doing so, slowly turn your head up, down, left, and right. Pay attention to the geometrical shapes and colors you see.

The Sphere-matrix is massive. You're at the very center of it. It goes with you wherever you go.

When you look to the sides, you can see that the matrix perimeter is not interrupted by the ground you're sitting on. Remember, it's a multidimensional energy system. It penetrates continuously through the Earth. Look underneath your body and you will become aware of a big circular shaped disc, about 70 to 90 feet in diameter. It is reddish/orange in color and has a particular thick consistency—this is the bottom funnel.

When ready, you can look up to view the upper funnel as well. Remember, there is no need to rush; this is all yours.

You are the extension of Source, and similar to the Creator, you are magnificent and divine.

The Secondary Merkabas were the ones I saw first. That was the beginning of what you're now learning here. Over the years, I became aware of the colors and its six layers.

Humanity has taken a big step away from the true essence of its existence, far into the materialistic world and the belief in imbalanced science.

This information can help bring back the understanding and awareness to all who seek the way back 'home.'

Become aware of your power and profound importance in this game of life and beyond.

Your DNA is that of royalty.

You are very important!

The benefits:

- Increase your capacity to heal yourself, others, and the planet.

- Learn a powerful healing modality.

- Become a manifestation powerhouse.

- Improve your channeling abilities.

- Clearer connection with your Akashic records.

- Increased level of bliss, joy, and compassion in your life.

Dear Soul, this concludes my chapter. I invite you to learn more about these subjects through my main website: Vort8x.com (Pronounced Vortex). There you will find classes, courses, sessions, presentations, and more.

I'm grateful and honored you are here.

Infinite blessings

Eddie BenAbraham

Eddie BenAbraham is a teacher, channel, healing facilitator, inventor, presenter, and author. In 2019, Eddie built Vort8x.com with a mission to assist fellow humans during the shift into Earth's new Golden Age.

Through his teachings of basic and advanced esoterics, Eddie offers his tribe the awareness and the means to consciously create a life of joy, balanced health, and abundance.

"My Entourage" is what Eddie calls his divine-support team. Using the art of reading Turkish coffee grounds, Eddie's channeled sessions and coaching programs give in-depth reading and can lead to profound realization and healing in your past, present, and future. One of the key subjects in Eddie's powerful courses and presentations is "The Anatomy Of Your Soul." This subject has been a passion from a young age, and today, it has developed into a critical part of understanding the divinity in our human experience.

In 2017, Eddie introduced to the world one of his inventions, "The Compassion Gauge Tool," with the help of his friend and master programmer, Peter Bakalov. The Compassion Gauge Tool can automatically detect and measure the level of compassion. Once the user clicks the button, the system recognizes their state of being and, in a fraction of a second, shows the level of compassion ranging from 1 to 10.

Eddie's most recent development is his connection with The Seven Founders - The Original Whales. The fascinating channeled information will be part of a six-book series—five workbooks based on his course, "Ascending Into Your Heart's Awareness," and the sixth about the Original Whales.

Eddie's ongoing work includes a wide range of subjects. You're invited to join the loving community on his online platform to connect with like-hearts. There you will find the services offered and ways to contact Eddie directly.

Please visit www.vort8x.com

We look forward to meeting you.

"You seek power, look within.
You seek love, reach within.
You seek peace, step within.
The world will follow."

~ Eddie BenAbraham

CHAPTER 3

SELF-CARE 101

LOVING YOURSELF FIRST

Maureen Mays

MY STORY

This was my first time on a flight with my kids. The words that stood out to me in the flight attendant's instructions were, "Put your oxygen masks on first, before helping others." Immediately a picture of me doing the opposite flooded my head. Although the kids needed to hear the safety briefing, it was more important that I not only heard it, but understood it. This is an important rule for ensuring survival. Why? Because if you run out of oxygen yourself, you can't help anyone else with their oxygen mask.

The phone's ringtone was extra loud that morning. I must have slept through the first and second alarms. "Hello," I answered, trying to sound like I wasn't just sleeping deeply and peacefully. I knew who it was. Who else would be calling me at 4:30 a.m.? It's the driver I hired to drive us to Ronald Reagan Airport, which is about 40 minutes away.

"Ms. Mays, I'm outside waiting." Wanting to cuss, I jump out of bed and respond. "I'm coming out; give me a few minutes." I heard him sigh, "Ms. Mays, I have others to pick up and I don't want you to be late for your flight. We have to hurry." He knew my response, "I'm coming," was a total lie. I was sound asleep along with my kids.

Running to the hallway, I yell, "Get up! Get up and grab your bags. We have to go now or we will miss our flight!" They immediately grabbed their things. However, to my surprise, they were already dressed. The drive to the airport was the nap we could not deny our bodies. We tipped the driver and began to run with our bags—two each, one carry-on and one checked bag.

I reminded them, "Listen guys, no huge liquids in the carry-on. That includes lotion soap or even the water bottle you're drinking. They will throw it away." Still sleepy, they nodded their heads okay. We all sat in the three-row seat, still tired. We wore pink matching Aeropostale shirts. My son is a team player. He wore his shirt like the cool guy that he is. My daughter is always sporting sunglasses. This was our first airplane ride together. Miami, Florida, here we come to enjoy our first cruise. "Hey guys, the flight attendant is about to speak. Listen up! Her message is very important in the event something happens."

The flight attendant showed us where the exits were by pointing her fingers to the left and right. Soon after, she demonstrated and instructed us on how to put our oxygen masks on in the event we needed them. "Put your oxygen masks on first, before helping others." Universally, this rule can be stated as: Take care of yourself first before taking care of others.

This is self-care 101—loving yourself first before others. You've heard it before; you cannot pour from an empty tank. We cannot love someone else without fully loving ourselves first. We have to think about our time, boundaries, physical needs, financial responsibilities, and mental capacities. However, we do the opposite all the time. We give to others what we don't have. Our hearts become empty. When we don't take the time to love the most important person—me, myself, and I—first. We then tend to blame the person we sacrificed for, helped, and provided assistance to. This vicious cycle is not functional. It's not beneficial. It doesn't support the healthy love we're trying to manifest within ourselves. I know this firsthand because I am learning how to love myself first minus the guilt.

As a mother, I had to relearn so many things before I embraced self-care. There were so many unrealistic rules I began to own. They were impacting how I loved myself. The definition of being a mother was replaced with great sacrifice. Of course, we know there will be some sacrifices, but when it impacts the well-being of our mental state and our physical capacities, that's when we have to reassess priorities. I had to allow myself to breathe. I had to let myself off the hook. I started going to therapy. The sessions always ended with homework. The assignment would be, to go do something fun or do something for me. This assignment was not easy. Between my schedule, and raising kids, there was very little time for myself.

The trip I planned for us was expensive. I worked three jobs to ensure the bills were paid. Yes, I worked three jobs. One full-time, and two-part time jobs. I wanted to ensure the trip was paid in full before we set sail. I wanted to make sure we had ample spending money. Do I regret the trip? Of course not, we had a blast. We made great memories. The thoughts, questions fall, are: Would I do the same for myself? Do I make those sacrifices for myself? Do I say "No" enough? Am I making sure that Maureen is living, experiencing, and enjoying life to the fullest? Simple questions, but we can get lost in this world where the things that are not taught are caught. I've learned some things that are not good, especially when it comes to loving myself first.

I want you to picture Cinderella. We all know the story. Two pictures come to mind when we think of the Disney princess. The one where she's living with the mice and forced to sleep with the cinders by the fireplace, which left her filthy. She also was told that she did not deserve to go to the ball by her stepmother. The other picture is when she is dressed in a beautiful gown, her hair done, and a chariot waiting to whisk her off to the ball. This narrative, of course, told her that she not only deserved to go to the ball, but she was worthy of fine clothes, even glass slippers. We all know when we look good, we feel good. Her godmother taught her a lot with the flick of her magic wand. In real life, we do not have fairy godmothers or magic to undo the trauma others inflict upon us. There may be some scenarios, upbringings, and people in our lives who loved us wrong. It may very well have been unintentional pain that left damage. It's never too late to learn a new thing. What things do you need to unlearn in terms of loving yourself correctly? The things I had to relearn were the following:

Rest is not a dirty word. We must learn how and when to rest. Rest is a synonym for God's peace. Resting in the peace of God is agreeing with his will and his ways in our lives. This peace will rejuvenate your spirit and mind. This is an important requirement for loving yourself.

Superwoman is a bad word. I no longer desire to be a fictional character that makes problems look easy. Running here and there to fix, repair, create, and heal everyone is not my job. But that's what I remember seeing growing up. I remember seeing so many women who were making things happen. They did this with little or no financial support. They did this with no team. Whether it's cooking Thanksgiving dinner with little help, taking care of a relative with little assistance, raising children, managing an office, or unrealistic work responsibilities.

Saying no is a superpower. I wish I learned this superpower earlier on in life. It would've saved me some trouble. Saying yes will put you in scenarios you were never meant to be a part of, especially if you're a people pleaser. The power of no is the best thing to not enable people.

When you enable others you hurt yourself. This is done by taking away from yourself. You prevent others from carrying out their responsibilities. It encourages behaviors that will become self-destructive. You heard it before. Stay in your own lane.

Self-care is not a selfish act. The majority of us believe this, but we often do the opposite. Doing something for myself for the love of me is in no way an act of me being selfish with my feelings, time, or money. Look at the following this way. I'm not feeling well. I have various symptoms, like a headache, weight loss, and pain in my chest. I schedule a doctor's appointment. I miss the appointment, I get critically sick, and someone has to take care of me. That is selfish.

THE PRACTICE

Putting this into practice is better said than done. First, relearn what self-care is to you. What are your requirements for loving yourself? What we think self-care looks like and what it actually is are two different things. Oftentimes we look at self-care as being the physical things. That is fine. However, just like in our Cinderella story, when the clock struck twelve, she was back to her raggedy dress and her dysfunctional situation.

To truly honor and love ourselves we cannot ignore those difficult conversations, unhealed trauma, health, and spiritual well-being. Facials, milk baths, manicures, new shoes, and hair appointments are great. I love those things too! It should all be included in your total self-care plan.

Loving you first will have you setting boundaries and being comfortable with saying the word "No" when it does not suit us.

We have to let go of negativity. Even the negativity that we say in play. You don't know what I'm talking about? I gave someone a compliment about a gorgeous necklace they were wearing. Instead of the response being "thank you," they responded in a light laugh, "It goes with the chunky body." I've done it too. Someone would say my hair is pretty and I would say, "Thanks, but it's falling out in the back." We tend to spotlight the negative in the positive.

Getting proper rest is important too. My author friend Kelly Meyerson is a sleep expert. Getting better sleep is one of her favorite things to discuss. We have to let go of the phrase: "I'll sleep when I die." What a cruel thing to say to yourself.

We must learn from our triggers instead of allowing them to cripple us. We have to have the difficult conversations. We have to allow ourselves a moment to feel the emotions, even if the emotions are false or make us cry. God made us. The Bible is full of teachings that command us to care for ourselves. Proverbs 4:23 says: "Above all else, guard your heart for it is the wellspring of life." This scripture states that we must take care of ourselves. We must guard, nourish, and care for our well-being because it matters to our creator. He made us in his image and his likeness. He has created a unique work in us. Our bodies and mind are our temples. This is his gift to us. We get the opportunity to be a good steward of this gift. He has a whole book about love. It can be found in the book of Corinthians, chapter 13. The first sentence opens with, "Love is patient." It then follows with, "Love is kind." Jesus showed us how we could serve God while taking care of ourselves. Throughout the New Testament, there are several examples illustrating Jesus taking time to get away from the crowds. He made this a priority. This time allowed him to pray, rest, and hear from God. He focused on being still.

Remember, I said self-care is not selfish. Loving yourself first is important. We cannot carry out the Lord's work if we don't first love ourselves the way our Father intended. When you practice self-care you can pour out the blessings from a full pitcher. That is not selfish. So just like on the airplane, let's put on our masks before we help the person next to us. In the same fashion, let's take care of ourselves and love all of ourselves unconditionally. I, too, am in practice with what I am speaking. I'm putting my self-care plan of loving myself first into action daily. My current self-care plan consists of therapy, weekly sauna time, journaling, prayer, rest, reading, painting, boundaries, special soaps, and candles. That self-love will in turn go the distance when it's time to love another. Self-love will manifest and pour into your soul full of joy, and healing. I met a special guy a year ago and I am now in a relationship. One of the best gifts that he gave me was the truth. When he got to know me one of the questions he asked was, when do I rest? When do I do something for myself? One of my favorite things that we do is go to the park. We pack an old fashion picnic basket with our favorite snacks and drinks. We walk, talk, and just sit. There are times when music is playing, or I am reading. Other times we sit in silence watching the world. We watch people play and walk their dogs, birds fly, and kids run. Most times we go to parks where there is water. The breeze off the water kisses our faces. This feels good to my soul, my mind, and my spirit. He helped me to find my laugh when I didn't know it was missing. He helped me with the homework my therapist assigned over and over again. We need people like this in our life. Loving me wrong was never done intentionally. I just lost my way in the hustle and bustle of life. I am learning to be better to myself. Please, be good to yourself. There is a love warrior living inside waiting to emerge to change the world with an infectious smile and a laugh.

Maureen Mays is a published author of *The Color of Life in the House of Mei, Love Still Smiles on Dark Days, Because She Had Something to Say,* and *Married, It's Complicated.* Writing has been a therapeutic pastime she discovered in her teenage years, and she rekindled her love for it after many years of being a closet writer. She now writes, paints, speaks, and encourages others to not only embrace their talents and dreams but, more importantly, embrace their God-given purpose. Maureen served in the United States Army Reserves. A mother of two children, they share her passion for entrepreneurship as they watch and strategically create, study, and embark on business opportunities. She is a resident of the DC Metro area. She attended Howard University and later graduated from the University of Maryland. She has a bachelor's degree in Human Resource Management. She serves as a board member of the Focus Recovery Center. Maureen also owns the Mays Collective consultant practice focusing on Human Resource solutions. She also owns Better Beginnings LLC, a real estate investment group. When she is not occupied with work, she enjoys poetry, writing, painting, cooking, live music, gardening, dogs, and enjoying life to its fullest. Maureen is available for speaking engagements, paint parties, and public appearances.

Connect with Maureen:

www.mmauthor.com

"I am measured imperfectly perfect sufficient to be just enough."

~ Maureen Mays

CHAPTER 4

LOVE YOUR BODY, MIND, AND SPIRIT
HEALING REDESIGNED

Birgit Lueders, MH, CCII

MY STORY

I am a *Love Warrior*. Every day I decide between love and hate. The moment I wake up, my mind starts racing. I walk to the bathroom, mindfully glimpse my reflection in the mirror, and wonder if I love what I see today. A few minutes later I think about my job; I remember stressful deadlines, and start feeling apprehensive about my day before it even starts.

Yes, we all fight our own wars within the battlefield of a dualistic mind. Our wars are right under our roof; our minds can either be a field of roses or a battlefield. Every single day, we have the choice to plant roses or fight wars within ourselves. Here is the problem. If we think certain thoughts over and over again, our subconscious minds believe this is what we want in life, so it will do everything in its power to change our external environment to match our inner world thinking. And voila, suddenly you live a life full of your worst fears or one filled with your deepest desires.

I learned this concept the hard way. After 15 years of marriage, sudden thoughts of discontent crept into my mind. I'd wake up feeling misunderstood, neglected, and alone in my marriage. Unfortunately, those thoughts kept popping up and lingered for over three years until my reality turned into a divorce.

I still don't know exactly who to blame, but living in the past has never helped anybody. The most important thing I've learned is that a tragedy like this can have two endings, forgiveness or hate—forever. I'm glad that my ex-husband and I decided to work on creating a great friendship that made it possible for us to become wonderful co-parents.

Because of this, over the six years after the divorce, our children enjoyed the attention of both parents equally. When we lived together, I was the children's caretaker, but after the divorce, each parent had to adjust their responsibilities. I learned to let go and focus more on myself on the days I didn't have the children, and he learned to be a full-time parent, which included cooking, laundry, driving kids to and from dance class, and organizing playdates. Now, after all those years, I can say that I feel happy and balanced, and I'm looking forward to the new adventures that life has in store for me.

My mother recently told me she is "so happy to have the old Birgit back." I was very surprised to hear her say this, so I asked her what she meant, and she said, "Well, the Birgit, I knew from back home, was always smiling and laughing. Sometimes she was even snort-laughing. That's the Birgit we all loved deeply. And then over the years, she became quiet." Her answer shocked me, but she was right. Over the years, I lost myself but thankfully found the old Birgit and became myself again.

To all the *Love Warriors* out there, if you have become quiet, frustrated, or confused about life, set out to discover why and fix it. You don't have to go through extremes like divorce. Nobody should ever go through this. Instead, find your laughter again by falling in love with yourself. Start listening to your body, mind, and spirit; that's exactly what I wish I had done earlier in my life.

Our soul speaks to us, but we're so busy getting through our daily repetitive lives that we don't pay attention to the subtle signs. Unfortunately, because of our inattention, the universe sometimes puts challenges on our path, forcing us to wake up from our monotony and change the course of our lives.

Many times, I've heard from cancer patients that their diagnosis was the best thing that ever happened to them! It made them realize that the things that seemed so important before the diagnosis really weren't important at all.

I once asked a lady who celebrated her 100th birthday if she had any regrets. She said, "I wish I would not have been so consumed with cleaning my house all day. I spent hours cleaning my house to keep it in tiptop shape. Why? I really don't know," she laughed.

If you come over to my house, you might notice a few dirty dishes in the sink, but I will always find a few clean cups so we can have tea together.

THE PRACTICE

Over the last 20 years working as a master herbalist and iridologist, I've noticed a common thread among people who suffer from several ailments. They never look inward. Instead, they try to find a quick fix outside themselves. It doesn't matter how many herbs or therapies they use; they don't seem to heal—until they peel the onion of discomfort, physically, emotionally, and spiritually.

We are a spirit in a human body, a body with energetic layers. If pain cannot be healed through the physical tissue, it might be stuck in either the emotional or the spiritual layer. Think of the phantom pain amputees experience. This pain feels like it's coming from a body part that's no longer there. How can they feel pain if there is no physical body part?

Working on all three layers simultaneously is what helps me guide my clients back to health. I call this process Redesigned Healing.

LOVE YOUR BODY

We all start life in self-love but often turn it into self-criticism. Children never have a single negative thought about their bodies. They understand that the body is them, so there is no "body" out there to hate. You can see it when you take photos of children. They seem so comfortable getting their pictures taken, but as they get older, they start comparing themselves to everybody else.

This is the end of self-love and the start of self-criticism. From that moment on, eating habits change, moods fluctuate depending on the number on the scale, and they delete pictures if the image doesn't look perfect. Unfortunately, this behavior is passed on from one generation to the next.

I once had a client who came to my practice because she felt extreme exhaustion, but her family doctor couldn't find anything wrong with her. It turns out that for many years she ran four miles a day and joined a bootcamp that met three times a week. She looked pale and frail to me, but insisted she needed to keep a slender figure. She seemed proud that extreme exercise and a strict diet made her stay close to the weight she had when she was 18. When I met her, she was 48 years old and had two beautiful teenage daughters.

I realized immediately that I needed to dig deep and discovered that she met and fell in love with the man she would marry when she was 18. Now, 30 years later, they've had many quarrels and don't even sleep in the same room anymore. She was worried he might leave her if she didn't stay skinny. Subconsciously, her mind created the thought that a skinny physique could save her marriage.

To redesign her healing, I suggested acupuncture for her energy body and hypnotherapy to release her thinking that love has something to do with her weight. After a few weeks of therapy, she felt better and could start my wellness program, which is all about nourishing the body.

Just like Hippocrates said, "Let food be thy medicine, and medicine be thy food." I needed to teach her that food is not her enemy, quite to the contrary. It's the expression of self-love and self-care.

People who go from one diet to the next never think of what food offers. Instead, they constantly worry about the calorie content, or whether it has gluten, fat, sugar, etc. Food should be seen for its energetic vibration.

A diet that is colorful, alkaline, and rich in fruits and vegetables adds energy to our body's cellular system. But a diet that is overcooked, microwaved, colorless, and has artificial flavors like MSG withdraws energy from our body's cellular system. As you can see, it's not about calories - it's about the energetic content of the food.

Imagine that after your workout, you eat a foil-wrapped protein bar produced at least six months ago. It's lacking in vibration and energy, but the manufacturer is promoting it as the best post-workout fuel because of its high protein and low sugar content. The problem is that after a long cardio workout, our body does not need protein. It needs glucose, not a protein bar filled with artificial additives, preservatives, and is wrapped in two layers of flexible polypropylene plastic with aluminum.

Cardio workouts empty our glucose storage in the liver and muscles. Glucose is vital for our adrenals and our brains. If we don't refuel our glucose storage, we end up with brain fog and our adrenal glands slowly shut down. The result is that our body starts showing signs of dry skin, chronic fatigue, hair loss, insomnia, weight issues, autoimmune disorders, and depression. These were all the symptoms that my client, who I mentioned earlier, experienced, but her doctor told her that these symptoms are normal in perimenopause and aging.

Once upon a time, we ate a banana or an orange after a workout, until the food industry introduced us to Gatorade and protein bars. Eating healthy is easy; just eat real food—food you can recognize and that has been around for centuries. For example, if you'd like to eat an apple, then eat an apple, not air-fried apple slices, applesauce with high-fructose-corn-syrup, or apple chips. Just have an apple.

So, I introduced my client to a variety of colorful vegetables, smoothies, stews, herbs, and juices, according to her Iridology Constitution. After several weeks, she felt more energized, happier, and stopped obsessing about her weight or how much or how little she ate. A body on a diet that is high in minerals, vitamins, and antioxidants has a naturally balanced appetite.

Once my client's physical body was healthier, she became more positive and hopeful. She felt confident enough to tell her husband how she felt, and together they went to couples' therapy and on a long-needed vacation to the Bahamas. A few months later, she felt more at peace with her marriage and even discovered a new passion for yoga and long evening walks with her husband and their new puppy.

If my client hadn't experienced extreme exhaustion, she would never have changed her diet and exercise routine, and who knows what kind of disease her body would have developed ten years later. Fortunately, she listened when her body whispered. She changed her self-destructive behavior to a self-caring and loving attitude.

TIP #1

**Give yourself the same care and attention
that you would give others,
and you will see how happy and beautiful
you will feel both inside and out.**

LOVE YOUR MIND

Did you know that every single organ has a specific emotion energetically attached to it? This is nothing new. This knowledge has been around for thousands of years and is well known in traditional Chinese Medicine.

For example, our lungs and large intestines are energetically connected with the emotion of grief. So, if somebody is going through an enormous amount of stress or grief (as I am writing this, the whole of England is grieving the passing of their beloved Queen Elizabeth II), these emotions will affect the strength and health of the lungs.

It is not unusual for a couple who've been together 50 to 70 years, to see the person left behind die of pneumonia shortly after the loss of their partner. I know many friends who lost both of their parents within a few short months of each other.

Consider the largest organ of our body, the skin, which is connected to the energetic vibration of irritability, like *somebody is getting under your skin*. Makes sense, right? So next time you have a rash, stop, and think about what is really irritating you. It's not the rash that makes you itchy; something or somebody else might be the cause of your itch.

Now think about adolescents. Most acne, a bacterial skin inflammation, shows up in the teenage years. That's the time when young people try to find and express themselves, but parents rarely allow them to do this fully. Those teenagers have no chance to rebel because they still live under their parent's roof. So, their skin gets inflamed because of the constant feeling of irritation or being upset by having to live by their parent's rules.

I'll give you one more example and this one is almost funny—grinding your teeth or getting lockjaw. Many adults nowadays wear retainers when they sleep because of their dentist's recommendation. The reason? So, they won't grind off their teeth while they sleep.

The jaw is connected to the *"grin and bear it"* attitude. I have had many clients who put up the façade of having a perfect life, especially through their social media, but at the end of the day, they grind their teeth.

If they *grin and bear it*, it means they have to accept difficult or unpleasant situations and that there's nothing they can do to make things better. They're not being honest with themselves, and the extra tension is released subconsciously during sleep by grinding their teeth.

In all these examples it doesn't mean your skin, lungs, or jaw will create a physical dis-ease instantly; it will only manifest as a physical weakness if you have battled with that associated emotion for a longer period of time. A guru once said it's like carrying a small pen in your hand. If you hold that pen for several weeks without ever putting it down, your hand will feel cramped and sore.

The most important thing we should do is acknowledge how we feel and be okay with feeling angry or anxious now and then. Anger and frustration are some ways the body communicates with us. I always suggest that my clients write in a journal. This helps them express their feelings by making regular entries in their journals. After several weeks, they can clearly see which feelings keep showing up. These are the feelings that need exploration. That is where healing will begin.

I once had a client who came to me after being diagnosed with breast cancer. This condition is associated with *the refusal to be nourished and nurtured by others.* Most breast cancer patients nurture everybody but feel guilty or ashamed to ask for affection or kindness from others. To truly help my client, I asked her to go to a grocery store. She wasn't allowed to take anything off the shelves without asking strangers to put it into her grocery cart, even if she could do it herself.

She hated that exercise and failed several times because she didn't want to be a burden to others. Once she got over her fears and worries, she could reach out and ask for help. She soon realized that the strangers she asked were eager and happy to help. After completing the assignment, she had a big smile and happy tears in her eyes. She said, "I never knew how much love people have towards strangers in need." She realized that for true self-care and self-love, it was alright to receive love and affection from others.

TIP #2:

Recognize emotions as they arise so they don't lay heavy on the organs. Remember, angels fly because they take themselves lightly.

LOVE YOUR SPIRIT

I mentioned at the beginning of the chapter that we are spirits in a human body. What I mean by this is that our soul uses the physical body as its temple or vessel to have an earth-based experience.

But unfortunately, we have strayed so far from our spiritual life that our physical body (temple) makes important decisions for the soul. Imagine purchasing a Tesla. Your car not only knows how to drive, but it also knows where to drive you to and when to pick you up before you even make a decision.

That car represents a life disconnected from its soul. It's a life that reacts and survives but is never in control of its circumstances and the world surrounding it. Our soul is our compass through life, but we need to tune in to it, to listen to it. Unfortunately, we can only connect to our soul when our mind is calm. The moment we get worried and stressed, we forget that this world is full of love, wonder, and magic.

The good thing is that it's quite easy to connect to our soul. All we have to do is sit quietly and close our eyes. It doesn't have to be complicated; you don't need to take a class for this and neither do you have to sign up for an ashram in India. Just sit and close your eyes.

For example, I recently had a client who came to me with severe breathing difficulties because of allergies. During our consultation, she told me she feels quite lost right now because her mother just died of lung cancer. Remember, lungs are associated with grief and the feeling of *having the wind knocked out of your sails.* My usual recommendations would have been herbs for lungs and flower essences for her grief. But this time around I suggested she just sit and meditate by looking into a candlelight.

A few days later, she called me and said, "You won't believe what happened." She told me she did exactly what I suggested and suddenly felt her mother's presence and her perfume. She had the feeling that her mother touched her shoulder and whispered: *Take a deep breath, I am right here with you, everything will be fine, I will always be with you!* The moment she received this message, her allergy attacks subsided, and she became a big believer in meditation.

But your soul doesn't have to connect with ancestors from the other side to feel guided. It can easily connect with its own Higher Self, or higher knowing. Our Higher Self is the wise being within all of us. It knows our purpose here on Earth, and our potential to live a fulfilled life through personal growth and self-awareness.

When you feel you're getting off your path, connect with your Higher Soul and let new thoughts come into your awareness through meditation. This is where you can find your answers to all the important questions in life. All your answers are within yourself.

TIP #3:

During times of hopelessness or fear, allow yourself to be guided through to your Higher Self, ancestors, God, or Universe.
Trust the higher knowing, surrender,
and take notice of the spiritual world around you.
Just because you can't touch it doesn't mean it doesn't exist.

I hope the various examples throughout this chapter resonate with you and inspire you to redesign your own healing. Remember, true healing has to come from all three layers: body, mind, and spirit. Only then will you be able to live a life full of health, love, and happiness. May your life feel like Heaven on Earth!

Wayne Dyer once said, *"Heaven on Earth is a choice you must make, not a place you must find."*

Birgit Lueders is the mother of two wonderful daughters, Emma and Lisa, living in Philadelphia, Pennsylvania. She is a certified master herbalist, yoga teacher, Iridology instructor, and wellness coach.

Birgit first learned the values of an organic herbal lifestyle in her home country of Austria. Since 2009 she has operated BirgitCare—a business focusing on health, wellness, and natural healing in Philadelphia, Pennsylvania. Through BirgitCare, she offers personalized wellness coaching to support her clients' emotional, physical, and spiritual wellbeing by using modalities like Iridology, herbalism, nutrition, and colorpuncture.

In 2012 Birgit founded the Center for Iridology, where she teaches Iridology courses around the world and annually in major cities in the USA. In 2020, during the pandemic she adapted her Iridology courses for online certifications and was able to move her wellness coaching program online.

Throughout the past ten years, Birgit has been a known speaker in her field at numerous national and international expos, and a best-selling author on Amazon, while being consistently featured on radio and TV. After being a fellow, a diplomat, and the vice-president of the International Iridology Practitioner Association (IIPA), in 2020, Birgit became President of IIPA.

Birgit Lueders, MH, CCII, Diplomate of Iridology

Connect with Birgit:

Website: www.birgitcare.com

Website: www.centerforiridology.com

Phone: 484-844-5710

"During times of hopelessness or fear,
allow yourself to be guided through to your Higher Self,
Ancestors, God, or Universe. Trust the higher knowing,
surrender, and take notice of the spiritual world around you.
Just because you can't touch it doesn't mean it doesn't exist."

~ Birgit Lueders

CHAPTER 5

A CELEBRATION OF LIFE
THE GIFTS OF GRIEF

Donna O'Toole, RN, B.Ed., Reiki Master,
Energy Healer, Intuitive

MY STORY

"You have ALS."

Did he just say what I thought he said? No! No, no, no, no, no!

The concept of the gifts of grief sounds crazy. I mean, who would ever think there could be a gift within any kind of loss, yet there can be colorful rainbows if you look for them.

I see the doctor moving his lips, but it sounds like his words are garbled, as if they were coming from a very long tunnel. Nothing is making sense, the second hand on the clock is moving, yet it feels like I'm frozen in some form of altered state. The doctor's words seem as if they're pounding on an empty beach. I will myself to snap out of it, knowing I need to understand what the neurologist is telling my husband. My handsome husband, the love of my life, has always told me he was going to live to be 105.

This just can't be happening to him.

My nurse gene kicks me back into reality and I'm awakened out of the misty fog. Time speeds back up and I'm thrown mercilessly into the now moment of truth.

I don't want to be here.

The average life expectancy for ALS is four and a half years. John's first symptom appeared two years earlier. I do the math quickly. *January 1999.*

ALS is a progressive nerve disease where the person loses control of the nerves used for movement, eating, speech, and even breathing. It literally can affect any muscle or organ within the body. The mind is not affected, leaving the person trapped inside of a body that does not function well.

I can't imagine John like this—so helpless—I can't go there.

My beloved John has never been ill in his life. Patience is not in his lexicon, and he was just diagnosed with a disease for which he will need every ounce of patience to deal with the constant changes to his body. *How can I help him?*

I pray, "Dear God, I do not have your wisdom or understanding. I ask for you to help him find patience, to give him added strength and courage. I pray that you grant me the physical strength to be able to take care of him. Please guide me, so I may be the kind of person he needs me to be. Thank you. Amen."

One word that most describes John is tenacity, and his tenaciousness served him well. The following life lessons and gifts were learned and shown over the last year of his life:

- Live in the present moment by never looking back.

  At 12 years old, John learned a valuable lesson while running a race. He told this story: "I was in the lead when I heard a runner's footsteps coming up on my heels. I turned my head to see where the runner was on the course, and because I looked back the runner passed me. I learned never to look back." As he lost mobility and physical strength, John looked positively at those activities he could still do. John was living in the present moment. This is not easy to do as I tend to think about the past or worry about the future.

  Really, isn't that what most people do? How much of my life have I missed as I spent time thinking about what could have been, regrets or making plans?

- You can choose because you have free will.

Surprisingly, John was not depressed. I asked him, "Most people with ALS experience depression because of the disease and losing their physical abilities. You're not depressed. Why?" He answered: "Let's say I only have one year to live. I could choose to spend that last year depressed or I could choose to live my life to the fullest each day. I choose living life."

A-ha! I choose how I show up every day, moment to moment. I choose how I feel and what I do. No one makes me do anything or feel a certain way. It is always my choice as I have free will.

- Living is hard; dying is easy.

Moments before John was taken off the ventilator to die, he pointed to everyone in the room and then wrote the word "lucky." The audible gasp from everyone filled my heart with love as I witnessed others understanding the depth of that simple gesture—John was the lucky one because of them. When he was able to speak after the ventilator tube was removed, he explained: "I am here to tell you that living is hard, dying is easy." Upon his deathbed, John was able to spend time with his family and friends and tell them what they meant to him and what he wanted for them in this life. John was one of those people who was larger than life. Upon his death, all three city TV news networks carried his death as their lead story. His life accomplishments were read into the state's congressional record. John touched so many lives as he lived every day to the fullest.

Did he know on some level his life was going to be so short, he packed so much into every day?

- Ambivalent feelings are okay to experience.

I vacillate between wanting things to go fast and then I want things to go slow. Fast, so he doesn't suffer long, and slow to cherish each moment we have together. Then I feel such guilt as I'm switching between these thoughts, until I am told by a therapist that these are normal feelings to experience. I remind myself: "Don't feel guilty! You're just being human."

- Helping others to accept.

When John just had hours to live, one older friend struggled as he said, "Why not me, why him?" My brother walked him outside in the hospital corridor and when they both came back into the room my friend was at peace. A few days after John's transition I asked my brother what he said that helped him.

He replied, "If God was growing a garden wouldn't he pick the prettiest flowers first?"

"But I'm pretty too!"

"Yes, but you still have work to do."

I could feel that remark hit me in my gut, and I knew it to be true!

From vast experience, I've learned that every person handles their life and dying process in their unique way. Let them take the lead to show you how they want your support. Ask them how you can be there for them.

- Caregiving is not for the faint of heart.

Caregiving is not an easy job as it can take a toll on your health. At times it will seem that you have lost yourself as the needs of others take precedence over your own. You find you take on their role as well as the one you already owned. So, it's important to make time for yourself. This will help carry you through the harder days.

When I re-examine this journey with John, I don't know how I did it. But I managed. The one thought that kept me going was: *How can I complain when he doesn't?* It was four months after his death before I didn't feel this overwhelming exhaustion in my body. I pushed myself to my physical, mental, and emotional limits. I didn't do it alone.

- It takes a village.

As the ALS advanced, it became clear I needed help in caring for him. That's when my village showed up. John's adopted family he called his brothers or sisters, or aunts and uncles. They came to help so I could keep him in our home, which was so important to the two of us. They came to sit with him so I could run errands. Businesses allowed friends to pick up food or gave me discounts and told me just to pay for it when I was in their area. When John was put on a special organic diet, my village brought groceries, cleaned 40 pounds of carrots a week, and donated an extra refrigerator. They danced with him when he was in a wheelchair, installed safety bars and ramps, and helped me pick him up from the floor when he fell. Whatever John or I needed they were there for us.

What a blessing it is to have these people in my life!

It takes two to tango, to give, and to receive. Honor those who give by receiving in gratitude.

• Cherish the simple things. Live in gratitude.

As you witness your loved one lose their abilities as simple as rising from a chair, bringing a spoon to their mouth, or turning oneself in bed, you realize how fortunate you are and begin living your life in more gratitude.

It's so easy to take who and what we have in our lives for granted. Take time each day to live in gratitude. When was the last time you told your loved ones and your friends what they mean to you, how they have enriched your life, and what you admire about them? Realize just how fortunate you are.

Value each small thing in your life, the simple everyday tasks, and the things you can do. Find joy within the small things.

Ask yourself: What is gratitude to me? What am I grateful for? Who am I grateful for? How do I show gratitude?

• Open dialogue is rewarding.

John and I talked about his terminal disease and what it meant to both of our lives. I cannot imagine going through this without being open with your loved ones. I remember how difficult it was when we opened this door of communication, but I know it deepened and strengthened our lives together.

John said: "When the time comes, I want you to let me go. I don't want to be on life support. I just want to be comfortable. I replied: "I don't know how to live without you, but I will find a way. I promise to let you go when you are ready."

John stated: "I only have one promise for you to make. I want you to move out of our home within the first year. I want you to have a life." I replied: "I promise."

He knows me so well! John realizes I won't get on with my life if I live in our home.

Talk frankly with your significant others. It launches avenues for great dialogue, including what they mean to you and what you want for them. These are cherished moments your loved ones will always remember. It's not how you physically look as you leave this earthly plane, but how you lived with the disease and how you showed up to live your precious life.

• Conversations with God are meaningful.

I no longer had time to pray as I was taught in church. I developed a special relationship with God as I learned how to bring him into my everyday chores and thoughts in a new and more meaningful way throughout the day. He became my trusted friend. I could say anything to him.

I am so exhausted. Can you help me feel rested? God, can you hold my hand tonight? I am so scared. How do I tell him I understand he can't hold my hand anymore when we walk, when I do miss that intimacy and special touch of his? I would listen for his answers.

What does grief feel like? Read this poem to yourself or aloud as each way will elicit different responses.

GRIEF

I had no idea
The gripping
Overwhelming
Sensation
Of Almost
Unbearable
Emptiness
Would be this profound.

No matter how
I prepared myself
I had no
Concept
No understanding
Of this deep
Heart wrenching pain.

Did someone just
Rip my heart out of me?

Can someone hear
The screams that
Are coming from me?
Or are they just
In my head?
No, my heart!

I can't believe
They are no longer here
I will no longer feel their touch
Hear their voice
Hear their laughter
Know their embrace.

I can't cry!
And then I cry
No, it's sobbing
From the depths of my soul
Deep from within me
This roar is felt
I can't stop crying.
When will this pain stop?
Will I ever laugh again?
Will I ever feel anything
But this pain?

I can't eat.
I can't sleep.
I can't function.

But I can think.
Oh, how I can think.
Thinking too much.
I don't want to think.
It brings memories
I just have memories.

Will I forget the sound
Of their voice?
Will I forget the feel
Of their touch?
Will I forget the
Image of their face?

This pushing and pulling
Inside of me.
Makes no sense.
Nothing makes sense.
Am I going crazy?

People want to help.
But they don't
Understand.
How can anyone
If they have not
Experienced this
This. . .
This tremendous loss.

I feel pain.
I feel nothing.
How can there be
Pain within this nothingness.
But, yet there it is.

I put on my strong face
Now in front of others.
Hiding my pain
Within me.
I know this is not good.
But I don't know how
To cope.
How to live now
Without them.

This grief
There is a whole
New meaning to
Grief.

Days are getting better
And then there are
Other days
Of darkness and pain.

I think I hear them
Or see their shadow.
Sometimes this
Gives me comfort.

There is a light coming
From time to time.
I start to function better.
Or am I fooling myself?

Intellectually I know
They would want me
To live life.

I start to smile
With memories.
I now know
Memories are
To be cherished.
It is what we have
In our relationships
With each other.
Shared memories.

Why does it oftentimes
Take grief
To know what
Is really important
In life.
What really matters.
Grief allows time
To define life.
Define love.

This gives me courage
To be me.
To find me
My authentic self.

Isn't it strange
That through their death
I get a gift
To find out who I am
So, I make time to find me
A new me.
I have days now
When I grieve
When I cry myself to sleep.

But. . .
I am getting stronger
Each day.

Finding a purpose
To my life.

Knowing I honor them
By living my life
Each day to the fullest
That is how
I show my love
Celebrate life.

THE PRACTICE

FINDING THE GIFTS OF GRIEF

Who would ever think there could be a gift within any type of loss, e.g., the death of a loved one or pet, the breakup of a relationship, or physical changes? How can anyone understand unless they have experienced tremendous grief?

Here are four ways for you to tap into so you can find the gifts of your grief:

1. Learn to be kind to yourself when processing grief.

    There is no timetable for grief! The five stages of grief are: denial, anger, bargaining, depression, and acceptance. You'll experience all these emotional stages and just because you get to acceptance doesn't mean you're done with grief. You will be triggered by something and find yourself back to anger or depression.

    I thought I was doing okay and now—why did you leave me? John, I am so angry with you!

    Rejoice and give yourself credit for each gain in your healing process. Remember to be gentle with yourself. Live one day at a time and give yourself permission to grieve.

    Don't be a hermit. Take advantage of friends' offers to do things. Find your friends who listen well. And ask for hugs as they are important and always welcomed!

Find a support group that is perfect for your needs. There are many out there!

Make decisions when you are ready to make them.

I don't want to give his clothes away just yet! Why are people pushing me to do this? I'm not ready to downsize right now. I don't want to put all his photos away. What do you mean, get over it?

2. Making time for self-care.

Put yourself as priority number one. This is your time. *What does me time look like? When was the last time I had a massage? Vacation? Meditated? Exercised? Lunched with friends?*

3. Finding yourself on the other side of grief. Discover who you are by asking yourself some questions:

   • Is there something I have always wanted to do?

   • What have I never had time to do before?

   • If I had an opportunity for a do-over, what would I do?

   • What is my life purpose?

   • What is on my bucket list?

   • What does a perfect day look like?

   • What would my loved one want me to do?

4. Celebrating their life.

You will find the right way to celebrate their life. I choose certain days of the year which were special to us. How will you celebrate their life?

CELEBRATION OF LIFE

A celebration of life
A day of remembrance
Honoring the person
You were
And the way you
Lived your life.

How you took the time
To touch someone's life.
The way you lived
Fully each day.
The positive manner you
Faced and endured
Life's challenges.

Your light shone brightly
And was diminished
Many years too soon.
You graced the world
A better place.
And your memory
Dwells in the
Hearts of those
You touched and loved.

You honor the person's life by living and celebrating your own life each day. Finding your rainbows will enrich your life.

How has grief touched your life? What gifts did you receive? I would love to hear your story.

Donna O'Toole, RN, B.Ed., Massage Therapist, Druid Priestess, Intuitive, Energy Healer, Awen Awakener.

After caring for her husband of 14 years, who died from ALS, Donna knew something was missing from western teachings. This led her to search and study across many fields. As a result, she merges the western and eastern philosophies to enhance and enrich how one lives their life.

Donna bridges this work with many other teachings as a Reiki Master, Karuna Reiki Master, Crystal, Sound and Color Healer, clearing and blessing homes and spaces, intuitive, poet, actress, singer, and guided meditation leader. She is in her third decade of embracing the healing arts, energy work, sound healing, crystal healing, crystal grids, Celtic and Irish study, druidism, and meditation, to name a few of her varied interests.

Donna's expertise focuses, as she feels called, on those individuals who need help with alternative healing options; transitioning from this earth plane; and those who have had the trauma of childhood sexual abuse.

Donna started writing poetry 11 years ago and found this method of writing, as well as journal writing, has led her to further healing for herself and her readers.

She also brings healing through guided meditations using focused "I AM" statements. Through Donna's years of stage and theatre work, she has learned how to use her voice and lends those talents to her voice-guided meditations, setting the right tone for delivery.

Donna truly believes it's important to live your authentic spiritual life and to be guided to dwell where it *makes your soul sing*.

Connect with Donna:

For further information and resources, go to

Facebook: https://facebook.com/AwenAwakener/

Email: AwenAwakener2022@gmail.com

"Each vignette of your life is woven by you to become a treasured tapestry embracing a landscape of air, fire, water, and earth, then spiraling into your heart center until it unites with the essence of your soul. Be mindful of what you choose to weave. Be mindful of those who are chosen to weave with you. Be grateful for your teachers and for the lessons you learn—living gratitude and loving wisdom."

~ Donna O'Toole

CHAPTER 6

YOU ARE AN ARTIST
UNLEASH THE CREATIVE GENIUS WITHIN

Phil Tavolacci, MSPT, Artist

MY STORY

"Look up!"

It was like someone had crept up behind me and shouted.

It was day number two of three days in the woods, alone and fasting. Fasting was new to me, and I feared I'd feel like I was starving, but I felt great.

I was participating in a Vision Quest on a 300-acre property in Ithaca, New York, led by a shaman. I'd never done a Vision Quest before. The total quest was seven days, but three of the days were solo in the woods and only consuming water.

I sat in an open field for much of day two, and it was a beautiful sunny day. There were no clouds in the sky, the air was fresh and crisp, and there were insects and various creatures creating a symphony of calming sounds. I took a short break from drawing in my journal and noticed a couple of birds circling at a distance. I was pretty sure they were hawks.

Around that time in my life, I was deepening my understanding and belief in the laws that govern the Universe. Specifically, I was delving into the Law of Attraction. I thought I'd practice what I was learning and attract these two majestic hawks to me.

I recall grounding my bare feet into the Earth and focusing all my attention on magnetizing these awesome creatures to me. I wanted to enjoy their beauty up close. The more I mentally focused though, the further away the birds flew. Within probably 15 minutes of this experiment wrapping up, both birds were totally out of sight.

Well, that was a giant failure! I was still quite skilled at being my own worst critic and judge at that time.

Frustrated and dejected, I sat down and returned to drawing. I loved drawing. Drawing was my happy place. I have no idea how long I was drawing but it was long enough to put me into a very trance-like state. It was at this point that the **"Look up!"** command entered my consciousness. This command was intuitive, mind you. There was no one nearby screaming at me.

Reflexively I pulled my gaze from my journal, snapped my head up at whiplash speed, and had one of the most breathtaking experiences of my life. The moment I looked up, an enormous hawk flew directly over my head. It was maybe 10 to 15 feet over me, and I saw every intricate detail of its stunning underbody and wings.

It was like time slowed way down, because what took only two seconds felt like a dramatic and cinematic two-minute experience. I've always been a pretty energy sensitive person, and it felt like my energy blended with the bird's energy in that spectacular moment. I'm fairly certain that if someone caught the experience on camera, I'd look like a five-year-old child staring in disbelief that the Tooth Fairy was actually in their room.

It seems silly writing the words, and it feels cliché to say it but—that was a life changing moment. It was also an experience that taught me a few important life lessons:

1. Just because something doesn't materialize immediately doesn't mean it's not coming.

2. Mental effort is nowhere near as powerful and effective as setting an intention, getting into a creative flow state, and allowing the Universe to leverage its powerful laws.

3. Art/creativity is a powerful pathway to accessing superpowers!

...

Artist (noun)- a person who creates art using conscious skill and creative imagination (Merriam-Webster Dictionary)

...

"Oh, cool! You're an artist!" exclaimed my friend who walked up behind me and glanced at my notebook.

"Nah, I just doodle pretty well I guess," I quickly retorted.

This brief conversation unfolded in the library at Ithaca College in 1990, where I was just beginning my journey to become a physical therapist. Art was the very last thing on my mind. I was laser focused on acing all my courses and eventually becoming a great physical therapist.

Art, however, was ever present in my life and partly responsible for getting me into a competitive academic program.

All my notebooks from the 3rd to 12th grade were full of notes commingled with drawings and doodles. I discovered at an early age that if I drew while I listened to and observed the teachings at school, I absorbed the information like a sponge. If I didn't allow the drawings to flow naturally, I had difficulty focusing and retaining information.

Thankfully, from what I recall, I was never asked to refrain from doodling or reprimanded for doing so. I was a straight-A student throughout all my schooling, so I guess my teachers recognized that whatever method I'd formulated for myself was working and why mess with it?

If I hadn't been allowed to draw all day long during school, I likely wouldn't have attained the academic record necessary to gain admission into the competitive physical therapy program I was accepted into.

Traumas in my childhood lead to chronic pain and dysfunction in my body from an early age. My choice to study physical therapy was partly fueled by a burning desire to resolve my own issues. I also loved anatomy, physiology, medicine, and helping people, so, from what I could tell as a teenager, physical therapy was a perfect option!

Fast forward to today, year 2022, and I'm scaling back on a wonderful and rewarding 24-year physical therapy career. From 1998 to 2004, I worked as a traditional physical therapist in various settings, including inpatient rehabilitation, outpatient orthopedics, and sports medicine. Then in August of 2004, I started a private practice that eventually focused on my evolving specialty—John Barnes based Myofascial Release (MFR). My practice, TAVO Total Health, continues to this day, and I still love helping people feel, move, and function optimally.

I've loved working in the healing arts as a physical therapist, but I put my non-therapist creative side on the back burner to focus on my therapy career. Being a manual (hands-on) physical therapist doesn't afford the same environment or opportunity school did to doodle or draw all day.

When the pandemic began in early 2020, I closed my private practice for two months. It was the first time in my adult life, and I'm 50 now, that my weekdays were not fully consumed by treating patients and running a business (or two). I had some breathing space to contemplate life on a broader scale.

Not too much breathing space, however! My husband, Jeff, and I began a lengthy process of adopting two incredible siblings, then five and eight years old, in December of 2019. As everyone can recall, this was just two months before much of the planet shut down due to the pandemic. It was a high stress time for sure as everyone in our household adjusted to a new life structure, and the world simultaneously acclimated in a million and one ways.

To manage my stress, I followed a persistent internal pull to the world of art. I watched hours of art related videos on the internet. I read art related books and poured over the Architectural Digest magazines I'd collected for years and hardly perused. I took a few online painting workshops. I drew. I bought painting supplies for the first time in my life because my medium had only ever been drawing with ink pens or pencils. And, finally, I started painting.

I immediately fell in love with abstract acrylic painting. I've always been fascinated by abstract art. It speaks directly to my right brain and subconscious. Much like drawing has allowed me to escape my very logical, analytical, perfectionistic, and often anxious mind, painting abstractly does this in an even more powerful and liberating way!

"I have no interest in portraying reality—that's what cameras are for," has frequently escaped my mouth when people have inquired why I don't draw or paint using realism. I'm in awe of artists who can accurately duplicate in paint, pencil, or another medium what the eyes see in our 3D reality, but it's not what I'm personally interested in—to each their own.

In June of 2022, I decided to gift myself an art website for my 50th birthday. One doesn't have to share or sell their creations in order to be an artist but that's the path I've chosen. I don't have much of a catalog of work yet, but you must start somewhere, right?

I've been encouraged by early successes and sales since launching my site, but the best thing, in all honesty, is stepping into the space of acknowledging and embodying: **I AM an artist!** I've evolved beyond the "Nah, I just doodle pretty well" phase.

One benefit of stepping in and embracing myself as an artist is the example it provides to our kids. I want them to know they can explore all aspects of themselves—all their talents, interests, and capabilities. I don't want to tell them; I want to show them. Both of our kids, eight and 11 years old now, embrace and revel in their artistic sides, and that is awesome to witness.

. . .

When you first saw this chapter title you likely responded to yourself immediately with one of two declarations:

1. Yes! I AM an artist!

2. Nope, not me. I don't have a creative bone in my body!

If you were a category one responder, then great. Please allow me to affirm that you absolutely are an artist. You didn't need affirmation though. No one could convince you otherwise.

If you immediately placed yourself in category two, then my goal is to gently and lovingly challenge your firm position.

As a child did you:

Doodle? Build structures out of available items? Dance? Play a musical instrument or sing? Find joy in any form of creating something that didn't exist prior to your participation or exploration?

If you flashed back and answered yes to any of these questions, then I'd suggest you are indeed an artist.

That child still lives inside of you. Are you willing to reconnect with that creative little genius? **Yes, I said genius!**

Walter Isaacson, a biographer of many well-known geniuses, explains that although high intelligence may be a prerequisite, the most common trait that defines a genius may be the extraordinary ability to apply creativity and imaginative thinking to almost any situation. ("What Makes a Genius? The World's Greatest Minds Have One Thing in Common" *Time; 1/8/2021*)

With that distinction, I'd have to say that almost every child is a genius, and every adult contains within them their inner child!

In 1992, NASA had a highly specialized test developed that would give them the means to effectively measure the creative potential of their rocket scientists and engineers. After the test proved to be highly effective at NASA, the test developers decided they wanted to explore and try to understand the true sources of creativity. So, they found 1,600 children between four and five years of age and ran them through the test. The outcome: **98% of the children scored at genius level!** (paraphrased from aNewKindOfHuman.com, 4/28/2017, *Study Shows We Are Born Creative Geniuses But The Education System Dumbs Us Down* by Gavin Nascimento)

THE PRACTICE

If you've read this far you are both a love warrior and an artist. You're a love warrior because you're bravely choosing to re-engage the child genius within and practice self-love through creativity! You're either an artist currently creating art or an artist about to create art! Either way, how about a bit of an art assignment?

Again, art can be shared or can be kept totally private. It's your art to choose what to do with even if the "do" is to stick it in a locked safe.

1. Carve out five minutes to complete a silent eyes-closed meditation in a tranquil and comfortable spot. Near you, set out a blank piece of paper (any size) and a few pens, pencils, and colored markers. This need not be exactly as I suggest here, but this is my recommendation:

   • Ask your inner child if they are willing to come out and co-create for a bit. Hint, they are almost always ready and willing when invited! And recall, children are creative geniuses.

   • Set the intention that once your meditation is complete, you're going to flow right into allowing something to show up on the page. Whatever shows up is what's meant to show up at that moment and it is art. It's one example of your art. You'll be using whatever art tools your intuition guides you to use.

2. Set a timer for 15 minutes and **go for it.** Be with your creative inner child and simply allow creative energy to flow through you and onto the page—no critiques, no judgments, no rules or parameters.

3. Once the timer goes off, take a minute or so to wrap up the piece. The timer alert is not a hard stop.

4. Take two to three minutes to simply be with the creation that emerged through you. Nothing to do; simply share the energetic space with this new, raw, one-of-a-kind piece of art. Consider signing and dating your creation.

5. Repeat one of these mantras (or one you create) three to five times with your eyes closed:

   • I am an artist, have always been an artist, and will always be an artist.

   • I am a human and humans innately create art.

   • Everything I create is art whether it's pretty, ugly, or anything in between.

6. Take two to three slow deep breaths. Breathe in through the nose and out through the mouth.

7. Finish your art session with a simple **thank you.**

Over the course of the next month consider doing the same exercise a few more times but with different creative pathways.

Maybe one day pull together a bunch of items (for example: stones, sticks, crystals, leaves, etc.), and after the meditation segment, construct something using all the varied items. Snap a few photos of your creation on your phone or with your camera.

Maybe another day grab scissors, 12-15 old magazines, some odds-and-ends, paper or fabric scraps, glue, and a piece of cardboard. Cut, arrange, and glue away until you've created something wild! Again, take some photos.

Possibly another time, get some multicolored yarn and weave it around and through all the furniture in one of your rooms. Zig and zag, and totally take the brakes off! Do this until you run out of yarn (and maybe even run out of breath). Again, photos.

Be creative and artistic even in your experimentation with mediums and projects. The possibilities are endless.

You don't need permission to do any or all of these art projects, but I'm going to give you permission anyway.

Let this be fun. Art is fun!

If you are someone who likes to share your creations or wants to push yourself out of your comfort zone by sharing these emerging creations, please send them to me at PhilTavo@gmail.com. I would love to see what you're birthing into the world!

One final reminder: YOU are an artist.

I dare you to say it aloud right now with me:

I

AM

An

Artist!

"The world always seems brighter when you've just made something that wasn't there before."

~ Neil Gaiman

Phil Tavolacci is a multipotentialite with many interests and creative pursuits.

Phil has been a physical therapist since 1998 and has owned and operated his private practice, Tavo Total Health, since 2004. Phil specializes in John Barnes based Myofascial Release (MFR), resolving issues within the connective tissue (fascial) system of the body. He works with his patients on multiple levels—body, mind, and spirit.

In 2013 Phil released the book *What's In Your Web? Stories of Fascial Freedom.* This is a story-sharing book versus a clinical or academic book. Stories shared by Phil, therapists, and patients all convey how fascial restrictions can be a source of pain and dysfunction and how MFR can potentially provide a solution.

Over the past decade Phil has also been helping to pioneer the emerging field of Nutrigenomics. Nutrigenomics is the science of how targeted nutrition directly impacts gene expression.

Phil has drawn, primarily with ink pens, all his life. In early 2020 he decided to delve into the world of acrylic paint on canvas and uncovered a love for painting. For his 50th birthday in June of 2022, Phil decided to fully embrace the artist within and launched **PTavo.art.** He has been told often that his art has a healing energy embedded within it.

Phil lives in suburban Maryland with his husband, Jeff, their two children, and their 20-year-old cat. They are a foster-to-adopt family and are eager to welcome a dog into their home soon.

Gifts for the first 50 people to join Phil's art list:

Receive a free 4"x6" high-quality print of "Sangria" if you go to **PTavo. art** and place yourself on Phil's art mailing list. Phil will periodically gift other items over time, so even if you're not in the first batch of 50 people, please still join!

"Just like snowflakes, your art is one of a kind. Every creation is one new possibility amongst infinite possibilities."

~ Phil Tavolacci

CHAPTER 7

MANIFEST ANYTHING
BE CAREFUL WHAT YOU WISH FOR!

Angela Orora Medway-Smith,
Cariad Spiritual, The Practical Mystic

"Ask for what you want and be prepared to get it."

~ Maya Angelou

MY STORY

"This weekend I'll be introducing you to all of my family," I told my boyfriend as we sped along the motorway to my family home in Wales.

He grunted, focused on the road ahead.

I gazed over at the sparkling lights of the city in the distance. *I have no idea why those words just came out of my mouth. I wish he'd slow down; the speedometer's reading past 110mph!*

We made the 200 mile journey in under two hours, unpacked the car, and entered the cold empty house; my parents were abroad. It was still early.

"Shall I call Bev and Jeff to see if they'll meet us for a drink?" I said.

He nodded in agreement. I headed over to use the phone and almost jumped out of my skin; it rang just as I put my hand on it.

"Is that Wendy?" an unfamiliar man's voice asked.

"No, it's Angela, she's not here right now. Can I help you?"

The line went silent for a moment.

"Angela, this is your grandfather, John. I was expecting to speak to your mother; your nana and I have come to find you."

I felt as if my heart stopped, my mind was racing.

"How did you get this number?" I asked.

"We drove to the village where you grew up from our home in Oxfordshire today and asked the newsagent about your mother. As we did, one of your uncles walked into the shop. He took us to his home and his wife gave us your mother's number. We were going to ask Wendy if we could meet you."

The string of events that led to this call was blowing my mind.

"Oh, I see. Where are you now?" I asked.

He replied that they were staying in a local hotel for two nights and we arranged to meet the following afternoon.

Nervously, I walked into the lounge of the small seaside hotel a few hundred yards from the house I grew up in.

The smell of stale beer hung in the air; the garish 1970s carpet stuck to my shoes as I opened the door. In the far corner sat my grandparents—tiny people with white hair and deep lines etched on their smiling faces that stared up at me.

I had no memory of these people; never even seen a photograph.

My father, Bryan, left my mother, his pregnant wife, and me, his one-year-old child, and skipped the country to Canada in 1964. There was no contact, no support, nothing. We were raised by our mother in our maternal grandparents' home. My mother remarried when I was a teenager; I loved my stepfather dearly, a kind and generous man.

My grandparents told me that Bryan, their only child, told them if they contacted us they would never hear from him again.

They told me of the times they secretly made the 200 mile round trip to watch us playing from a distance, my nana, Ivy, describing how I wore my hair and clothes as a child.

I reeled from this disclosure. *They had spied on us! The thought of being watched as a child felt quite disturbing.*

Ivy sobbed, pleading, "We want to make it up to you, to get to know you. We have always loved you." My heart went out to her.

"This is a photograph of your father. He is overseas working in Nigeria. He's always overseas with his work."

She handed me a picture of a tall, tanned, dark haired man with my face.

I stared at the photograph.

I had never seen a photograph of my father.

Time stopped.

I had done it.

After countless years of sitting in libraries looking through phone directories, of praying, of yearning, of checking the mail on my birthday, and opening every Christmas card that dropped on the mat. I had done it. The manifestation techniques I had learned less than one month earlier and put into action worked!

We swapped details; I promised to keep in touch and visit them. They lived just an hour from my home in London.

A few weeks later, I sat on their chintz covered couch while their eager poodle yapped loudly, jumping up at my legs for attention.

Sunlight streamed through the window of the small bungalow in the ancient Oxfordshire market town. Every surface was covered with ornaments. My nana chattered constantly since I arrived, making up for lost time.

"So, does my father come home very often? I'd like to meet him," I asked.

They looked at each other intently. "She needs to know," my grandfather said.

"The truth is, we're not speaking to him," said my nana. "We don't get on with your father's wife."

Well, it's been 23 years and my mother has remarried, so why wouldn't he have married again?

"They have three children, a daughter, and two sons, and we're not allowed to see them either," she added.

"Margaret went with him to Canada and they returned to Bristol for your sister to be born."

I felt as if the room was spinning. Time stopped yet again. *He left his pregnant wife and baby daughter and moved to Canada with another woman!*

The veils of my illusion of this man who gave me life began to fall away. My childhood self built this imaginary picture of a misunderstood young man who removed himself from my very strong matriarchal family to live almost 4,000 miles away to heal, not to run away with another woman and bully his parents into also abandoning his other children. There was just a year between my sisters' birthdays.

She continued, "He gave a false name on their birth certificates so that he couldn't be found by the courts."

My grandfather couldn't look at me. He stared at his feet, stroking their poodle in his lap.

I steadied myself. Listening intently as the facts emerged.

I was told that his new family lived in Derbyshire, my sister in London. So I asked for my father and sister's addresses and said I would write to them.

The remainder of the afternoon was spent being shown photographs of my father as a child, their extended family, and stories of my mother, how much they adored her and had missed us.

I wanted a relationship with my father so badly I was prepared to forgive everything.

My mother had been silent about his departure. All I knew was that he left us and moved to Canada, didn't turn up for the court hearing for maintenance, and she divorced him after seven years for abandonment (which in the 60s was how long she legally had to wait). Her silence allowed me to build up an illusion, my own fairy story.

I returned to my London flat and absorbed all of this information.

I had three siblings! How would I feel if I was presented with two older sisters? How could I tell my mother, wonderful stepfather, and my sister? How would they feel? Would my father even want to hear from me?

These were such huge questions my conscious mind didn't know where to start, so I meditated for clarity.

I picked up the phone to call my mother and tell her. Her reaction shocked me, as she laughed heartily.

"Good luck to her! I hope he hasn't raised his fists to her too, and stood over her while she ironed his shirts so he could go out and meet other women. We are the lucky ones. Be careful of that man. He is not what he seems."

Why hadn't she told me he'd beat her? It might have made a difference to my wanting to meet him. Could I forgive him for that? I still had this chasm in my life that needed to be filled by knowing the man who had given me life.

My younger sister's reaction was similar: "I'd like to meet our grandparents, I feel sorry for them, but I never want to see or hear from him! He didn't even wait to see me born."

I sat down to write a letter to my new sister explaining I just wanted to get to know them all, not replace them; less than a week later she was sitting on my couch in my modern, airy London flat.

"I've known about you since I was a teenager," she told me. "Dad said that your mother was unfaithful and her new baby wasn't his, which was why he left," she said.

Liar!

"That's not true," I said, and showed her a picture of our sister. It was obvious that we three were all sisters; we had the same eyes, his eyes. Both my sisters were blonde like their mothers. I was the only one with his dark hair.

"Dad will be down in London in a couple of weeks, and you can meet him then," she said.

So it began, meeting Bryan, my birth father, opening my heart to him, and trying to build a relationship.

Oh, how I had wished for this.

I thought finding him would help me piece together who I truly am.

My relationships with men were affected by being abandoned. I realized that throughout my life I tested every relationship and pushed partners away to see if they would also leave me.

I subconsciously believed that men were not to be trusted; they would leave. It was dangerous to love them; your heart would be broken. My adored uncle and maternal grandfather's deaths when I was a child cemented this inner belief.

I hoped that getting to know my father would help heal this part of me, the abandoned child.

Over the course of the next few years I got to know Bryan. Meeting him as an adult gave me a different perspective.

I opened my heart and received nothing but half-truths and lies. My heart was broken over again.

I was indeed lucky to have been raised without this man in my life.

My maternal grandmother had always said, "A leopard never changes its spots." I prefer to give people the opportunity to change—to be honest— and to treat others with love and respect.

But every time I opened my heart to my father he let me down, attempted to manipulate me, and lied.

Eventually, I chose to step away from the relationship. This time it was my choice.

My value as a human being was not defined by being abandoned. I was not unlovable.

Several years passed, and yet another surprise awaited when I stood in my kitchen and opened a small brown envelope to find a beautifully handwritten letter.

"Dear Angela, I am your sister. I was given up for adoption in 1960," it began.

That man is unbelievable! Even before he married my mother, he was engaged to another woman and left her when she became pregnant! This leopard had certainly not changed his spots.

I forgave my father for abandoning me many years ago. I have forgiven him for all of the lies he told, and all of the manipulation attempted as an adult.

Just one of his six children speaks to him now; he's in his 80s and my wish is that while he still can, he makes peace with all of his children and begins to make a start on dealing with the karma he's racked up in this lifetime.

I do not regret manifesting his presence in my life when I did. However, if I had my time again, I would do things differently.

I would have considered everybody who was likely to be touched by this manifestation and used a key statement in my manifestation process.

"I manifest this for the highest good of all and harm of none, in accordance with the will of the Divine and the will of the higher self. This, or something better will manifest for me."

I see this human life as a school, and the lessons we learn take us from kindergarten through to university. I believe we choose many of the experiences that shape us, and that I chose the experience of abandonment to learn more about myself.

There are some people who are just not meant to remain in our lives. Learning to let go when a relationship is not in our highest good was also a valuable life lesson this experience provided.

Manifesting my father's presence in my life was a huge lesson for me! I innocently expected him to love me, to have a heart as open as my own.

I'm much, much wiser because of this experience, and my life is much richer because of the relationships I built with my paternal grandparents and my half-siblings who I love dearly.

I did not receive the love I truly wished for, but actually much more love than I could ever have imagined.

When you open your heart to love, are broken, heal, and get right back up, you become a love warrior.

Love is all there is.

THE PRACTICE

I've adapted the manifestation techniques I learned almost 40 years ago and made them my own, creating a step-by-step process to simplify and speed up results.

I am very, very careful about what I ask for because my technique works very fast!

For example, my last major manifestation, to find a new home and new job worked within 72 hours and was fully implemented in under six weeks!

Taking your time to drill down into exactly what you wish to manifest, its full impact and the finer details, is in my view, essential.

I'm going to share my simple process with you here.

THE CARIAD PROCESS

1. What exactly do you want to manifest?

    This is the who, what, why, when, how; all of the detail. Be smart, specific, measurable, achievable (believe anything is!), realistic (most things are!), and set a timescale.

2. Who will it affect?

    This is the "Eagle Eye View" of the impact of your manifestation. Use a mind map to help you see the bigger picture of your new reality.

3. Engage support.

    Time your request to make use of moon cycles and find the correct ascended master, angel, or archangel to have in your corner to support your manifestation request.

4. The visualization.

    At the appropriate time, make your request, using the statement:

    "I manifest this for the highest good of all and harm of none, in accordance with the will of the Divine and the will of the higher self. This, or something better will manifest for me."

    Visualize or imagine that your wish is your reality. Engage all of your senses, and ensure your request is timestamped.

For example, visualize yourself walking into your new home. Run your fingers along the walls and the fabrics of the furniture. See your things in place, hear your music playing, smell the coffee brewing and sit down and taste it, see a newspaper on the table or a calendar on the wall with the date on it and feel the joy in your whole body of this new reality.

5. Finally, use the energy of sacred geometry to speed up the process. The sphere and cube have immense power; use them to speed up or halt processes.

Five simple steps to manifesting anything; but be careful what you wish for!

I have a beautiful workbook available to download which you can use to organize your thoughts and formulate your request to the universe.

You can find it at: https://www.cariadspiritual.com/lovewarriors

I wish you an abundance of good health, love, and joy. As Maya Angelou said:

"Ask for what you want and be prepared to get it."

Angela Orora Medway-Smith, The Practical Mystic, is a spiritual channel and teacher, master healer, Life & Soul Alignment Coach, and retreat leader from Wales. Her business is called Cariad Spiritual and she works in person and online spreading the light at workshops, festivals, and retreats internationally.

Cariad is a Welsh term of endearment derived from caru—to love. It reflects who she is, a spiritual being who works from the heart with love. Holistic healing is her passion; she's set up healing clinics and created holistic events and festivals raising money for charity, as well as training hundreds of healers, and providing thousands of clients worldwide healing and guidance from spirit.

Angela helped found Divine Energy International, a worldwide membership non-profit for energy healers. Its vision is "A world where energy healing is for all." She's on a mission! Changing the world one person at a time.

Angela is incredibly blessed to be a direct channel for the Angelic Realm and ascended masters and has published two channeled books *The Book of Many Colours: Awaken Your Soul's Purpose With The Divine Rays* and *The Book of Many Flames: Everyday Alchemy Using Esoteric Energy.*

She is also Co-Author of three #1 International Amazon Best Sellers *25 Tools for Goddesses: Volume 4 of the Wellness Universe Ultimate Guide to Self-Care, Strong Mothers: More Than A Survival Guide* and *A Journey of Riches: Awaken to Your Inner Truth.*

Angela offers spiritual consultations, Life & Soul Alignment Coaching, mentoring, retreats, healing, healer, and intuitive development training worldwide.

When she's not supporting others, or with her family, you can usually find Angela by water, walking along the banks of the Thames which flows near her London home, along the beach close to her home in Wales, or out in nature.

Connect with Angela:
Website: https://www.cariadspiritual.com/

"Invoking the flame of universal consciousness and basking in its fire will remind you that you are one with All that there is. Be reminded dear child, that every thought you have, every deed, action, every manifestation that you create, affects the consciousness of All that there is. We speak not only of the planet you exist on; we speak of the Universe in its entirety when we speak of All that there is."

~ The Archangelic Collective The Seraphim
The Book of Many Flames, channeled by Angela Orora Medway-Smith

CHAPTER 8

FINE IS A 4-LETTER WORD
SUPERCHARGE YOUR LIFE WITH GRATITUDE

Lori Saitz

MY STORY

"A month-long sabbatical? You're taking off a whole month?"

"Yes, yes I am."

"And you're taking the cat on a road trip?"

"Yup, 19-year-old Panther is coming with me."

"What are you going to do?"

"I'm not 100% sure yet. What I do know for sure is continuing on this current path is completely unsustainable."

There was very little fun or joy in my life. I was tired—physically, mentally, and emotionally exhausted.

The irony of all this is, I teach people to get quiet enough to hear their inner voice and learn to follow it. I also guide people on how to deeply *feel* gratitude so they can manifest faster.

But there was an obvious disconnect in my own life.

How did I let this happen?! How did I get here?

My 22-year marriage ended before the pandemic. During this difficult and emotional time, I moved across the country and back again trying to gain perspective.

Why couldn't I have been a better person?

Now that I was living alone, I threw myself into my business.

It was my habit to get on my computer by 9:00 a.m., write a LinkedIn post, share content on Facebook and Instagram, check and respond to email, do four virtual coffees back-to-back, host interviews or write the show notes for my podcast, guest on other people's podcasts, attend networking meetings, and add a multitude of other activities to my calendar.

As a dedicated and disciplined gym rat, I'd drag myself to Pure Fitness around 6:00 p.m. for a 60–90-minute workout, then come home, make dinner, and sit in front of the computer working until bedtime at 11:00. None of it was delivering the results I hoped for. But I kept doing it.

If I just put myself out there more, show up in more places, and reach out to more people, things will change.

When a business coach promised to help me get more high-ticket clients, I pulled out the only credit card that wasn't close to maxed out.

If this woman tells me to bark like a dog, I'm gonna do it.

Now I was sending 50 LinkedIn connection requests a day and starting conversations with people who accepted, in addition to all the rest I was already doing.

In theory, those conversations would turn into sales calls and then into clients. The problem was this method wasn't my style at all. So, I struggled to find the time and interest in doing the reach outs.

My phrase for the year was "ease and flow," but I wasn't even close. I wanted to find it and knew I needed to make a change to get there.

The sabbatical idea reared its head during a conversation in May with Julie, host of the podcast *Wake Up with Gratitude.*

"I'm shutting down my business and taking the whole summer off," she shared. "I'm disconnecting from all social media and spending the time relaxing and rediscovering what brings me joy."

Julie had been inspired by a Brené Brown article titled "Creating Space," in which Brené wrote about taking a 14-week sabbatical.

I'd like to take extended time off. But I can't. I need to do all the things. And what do I do with the cat?

A few weeks later, I interviewed Chris Schembra for my podcast. The author of *Gratitude Through Hard Times* and *Gratitude and Pasta*, shared what led him to an act of non-suicidal self-injury. "I've preached it. I've taught it. I've promoted it for all these years. And yet somehow, I'm the ungrateful man. I became the most recent victim of ingratitude."

By mid-July, I began to see I was losing connection to gratitude too.

I can't go on like this. Life is supposed to be fun. I'm not having fun. What's the purpose?

During one of the many virtual networking coffees I scheduled, Elaine excitedly mentioned the sale of her house.

"I'm eager to set off on a year-long journey in my motor home," she enthused.

What the hell?! Am I the only one not taking some fucking time off to find myself?! What would happen if I stopped living like I was always pushing a rock up a hill?

That's when I decided to say, "Fuck being fine," and started planning my journey back to a gratitude-focused life.

This trip would be an experiment in learning to allow ease and flow— following my intuition and staying open to possibilities.

I blocked off the month of August from any new appointments. I kept two already scheduled podcast interviews.

"What about publishing new episodes to my podcast? I can't take a break from that."

"Yes, you can. No one will notice," my wise friends insisted.

Now, where to go?

The answer was largely determined by where I could go with a 19-year-old cat.

Three months before, 12-year-old Karma unexpectedly passed. Panther missed her cat sister. There was no way I could leave her alone with a cat sitter. Plus, she required some pretty intensive care to ward off the effects of chronic kidney disease.

"She would rather be with you than anywhere else," my animal communicator friend assured me.

I guess I'm doing this road trip with the cat.

Cincinnati isn't first on everyone's summer vacation list, but it was on ours because my friend Jen welcomed both of us with open arms.

From there, we set off in the direction of south Florida, Panther's birthplace, to visit other friends and see my dad.

I thought we'd take I-75 through Atlanta. But sitting in a Cheddars restaurant in Knoxville while Panther violated hotel policy by staying in the room alone, I double-checked our route on Waze.

Now it was taking us through Asheville, Spartanburg, and over to I-95.

That's odd. But if we go that way, we can see Debbie on the coast of South Carolina.

I felt a wave of gratitude for this turn of events that would allow us to unexpectedly get to see my high school friend.

In the morning, Waze again instructed me to take the I-75 to Atlanta.

Nope, you already showed me this other way. There must be a reason and I'm going to follow my intuition.

As I accelerated onto the highway, a loud, airplane engine noise roared from the rear passenger side wheel.

Fuck! We do not need this!

I continued, finally pulling over at a rest stop near Asheville to see if I could find the problem. Since I didn't see any issues and the car was driving okay, I kept going. The noise didn't seem to bother Panther, but it was annoying me.

One of those podcast interviews I'd left on my calendar was for this day at 2:00 p.m. I needed to be somewhere with a stable internet connection.

I should be able to get to a coffee shop in Spartanburg by then.

Another hour later, I had a flash of insight.

You could stop at a Hyundai dealership and they could check out the car. They have wifi—two birds, one stone.

I called the closest one.

"Oh, honey, I can't get you in before Thursday at the earliest."

It was Monday.

I called the next closest one, in Spartanburg.

"I'm on a road trip with my cat. There's a sound like an airplane engine coming from a rear wheel. Any chance you can take a look?"

"Sure, I can fit you in whenever you get here," he said.

"To confirm, you do have wifi, right?"

"Yes, ma'am."

I handed my keys over to Alex at 1:48 p.m., plugged in my computer, parked Panther's carrier on the desk next to me, and logged on to the live interview at 1:59.

The dealership manager walked past, pointed at Panther, and practically squealed, "Oh, look, a cat!"

My host Paula started the conversation with, "Let's talk about how to stay calm and grounded no matter what's going on around you, Lori."

Seriously?! Considering I just made it onto this call with less than 60 seconds to spare and am sitting in the middle of a busy South Carolina Hyundai dealership, with a 19-year-old cat who may need to use the litter box, and feeling surprisingly calm and grounded, I'm well-qualified to address this.

"Yes, I've got the perfect example of that right here!"

I went on to share the saga and it made for a powerful podcast episode.

The car was out of alignment, which they could fix (thanks Kentucky highways). That noise, though, was caused by a bad wheel bearing, for which they'd have to order parts. The good news was, it wasn't a safety issue.

We were back on the road in a couple of hours. I saw how the Universe had my back and recognized the feeling of gratitude, ease, and flow.

Because this time was about allowing myself to have fun and feeling what it's like to live with ease and flow, there wasn't any agenda. After Panther and I arrived in south Florida, our host Christine and I pondered how we could play and made a list.

"Paddleboarding," I suggested. "And The Food Shack!"

"Want to take a pickleball class?" Christine asked.

"Yes, and let's get a massage too."

Amidst the days of ice cream, Thai food, and a lunch on the Intracoastal with my dad and his wife, I was able to reconnect with a part of my former self.

Having lived in Florida for 11 years a decade ago, I was also grateful to put my car in the hands of my trustworthy former mechanic, Steve, who I refer to as the car whisperer. I was amazed at the serendipity of it.

Sitting at lunch with my friend Evan, while Steve worked on my car, we discussed this sabbatical idea.

"I feel like I already live the sabbatical life," he said. "I have breakfast with different friends a few times a week and work until about 2:00. Then I go do something fun and relaxing. If I feel inspired, I may come back and work for another hour or so in the evening. That way I'm always refreshed for the next day."

Holy shit! This is brilliant. I want to live the sabbatical life too. Not just a month-long road trip, but everyday life.

Thank you, Universe. Once again, things work out when I allow myself to live joyously and in gratitude.

A few days later, I got a call from an acquaintance I met at a conference five years ago. He invited me to partner with him on what sounded like a fun and lucrative project.

I wasn't out there looking for this opportunity. I wasn't pushing to make anything happen. Because I was living in joy and gratitude and flow, it "randomly" showed up for me.

Two days before we were leaving Christine's, I still didn't know where we were going next. I was hoping our next destination would also randomly show up.

I Googled "Best beaches on the Gulf Coast of Florida" and was trying to narrow down the list.

Evan mentioned taking a writers retreat on Anna Maria Island. My friend Julianna agreed it was a beautiful spot.

"I have a feeling that's where you should go," she said.

But I wasn't finding the cute, cat-friendly, short walk to the beach cottage I wanted.

In my morning meditation, I got the strongest sense of surety I'd ever felt before and set the intention to find the perfect place on Anna Maria Island. In fact, it wasn't even like *I* set the intention. It felt as if it was set for me.

I came out of the meditation, hopped online, and looked again.

A bit of sleuthing led me directly to the perfect cottage!

I danced out of the bedroom, laptop in hand, into the kitchen where Christine was making a smoothie.

"What are you so excited about?" she asked. "What did you find?"

"Look at this cottage! Look at the courtyard!"

"It *is* gorgeous," she concurred.

I put in my reservation, we were granted early check-in, and Panther and I were set for our next destination.

Words cannot describe the tsunami of gratitude that washed over me.

Anna Maria Island is an absolute paradise! Panther agreed. As she explored the tropical, mostly enclosed courtyard area, she was likely thinking, *I'm outside! Look at these yummy plants! Oh, and lizards! Lizards are fun!*

Once again, I was proving to myself that manifestation through meditation and visualization works.

Sitting with my toes in the sand, basking in the beauty of the sun reflecting off the water, I took out my phone to take a picture.

That's when I saw the message: "I was referred to you. My organization has a large group of clients who can use your services. We would like to partner with you to develop some programs to teach them to reduce stress and incorporate more gratitude in their daily lives."

Once again, I wasn't out searching for this opportunity. It came to me when I was living in gratitude, ease, and flow.

On my last day in the cottage, I sat on the couch, reflecting on the previous month's events. Tears filled my eyes and gratitude filled my heart.

How lucky that Panther and I got to live this adventure?! All these synchronicities and coincidences happened when I wasn't even trying.

It turns out that working hard and doing more isn't the path to success, even though that's what I was taught. Breaking out of unproductive routines, finding the courage to say, "Fuck being fine," and replacing bad habits with more joyful activities *is*.

THE PRACTICE

You don't have to go on a one-month sabbatical road trip with a cat to start living more joyfully and in gratitude. One of the most powerful practices I've implemented myself and assigned to clients is the one I'm sharing with you. Every single one of them reports back their surprise at how tremendous an effect it has on them and their recipients. I encourage you to not just read about it but take the time to do it.

Start by thinking about the people who've influenced your life. Who comes to mind when you reflect on those who've helped shape you into the person you are today? It could be a parent, partner, teacher, neighbor, friend, or anyone.

Make a list. Then choose one who's had the most profound impact on you and whom you've never thanked.

Write a letter of gratitude to this person, preferably handwrite it.

In it, share not only *that* you're grateful, but *why* you're grateful. Let them know specifically how their words or actions affected you.

Then put it in an envelope and mail it to them—old school.

When my client Amelia first got this assignment, she struggled to come up with anyone who'd had a positive influence on her life.

"Keep thinking about it," I encouraged.

A few days later, she came back.

"I wrote a letter to a former co-worker at my last job," she reported. "She bullied me so badly that I ended up quitting. I've always held a lot of anger and resentment toward her. Now I feel like a heavy weight has been lifted off my shoulders. I will never look at life the same way again. Because of her, I started my own business. I'm grateful for that."

When I speak on stages, I tear up every time I talk about that story because of the life-changing impact this practice had on Amelia.

Others who've done it report similar results.

Gratitude turns hurt into healing.

And this practice doesn't only benefit you. It's incredibly touching for the recipient as well.

Another client, Kevin, reported, "My sister just broke down in tears. She was so moved by my letter." His relationship with her is now closer than ever.

Gratitude strengthens connections.

Before you get all in your head about how awkward it will feel to share your feelings of gratitude with someone in this way, know that most people overestimate the awkwardness factor. Once you do it, you'll see those fears are unfounded.

What if my handwriting sucks?

Do the best you can. If it's horribly illegible, write your thoughts by hand first. Then type them up. At the least, hand sign the letter.

What if my chosen recipient is no longer alive?

See if you can choose someone who is. If you're compelled to express your gratitude to someone who's passed on, write your letter. Read it out loud as if they are in front of you. Then release the letter to the Universe in whatever way you feel is appropriate.

Go now! Before you get distracted. Get a card or sheet of paper and a pen. Put your feelings into words and send them off.

In the words of Ralph Waldo Emerson: "You cannot do a kindness too soon, because you never know how soon will be too late."

Let me know how it goes. I'm genuinely interested in hearing about your experience.

Lori Saitz is the founder and CEO of Zen Rabbit and host of the podcast *Fine is a 4-Letter Word.* An award-winning writer, speaker, and broadcaster, Lori is on a mission to teach the world to be calm and grounded no matter what's going on.

As a nationally recognized gratitude and meditation expert, she guides entrepreneurs and corporate teams from stressed and chaotic to peaceful and focused—which allows them to increase sales, enhance relationships, and improve overall health.

Her F*ck Being Fine and Living the Sabbatical Life programs provide tools and techniques for recapturing joy and living in flow.

When she's not working, you can find Lori in her sanctuary, aka the weight room at the gym. She also loves cupcakes, Thai food, and classic rock music.

Connect with Lori:

Email her at Lori@ZenRabbit.com. For more resources, including a 6-minute gratitude meditation, go to https://ZenRabbit.com/LoveWarriors.

"You'll always find exactly what you're looking for.
Look for gratitude in every situation and you'll attract more
things for which to be grateful."

Lori Saitz

CHAPTER 9

RUTHLESS LOVE
OWN YOUR INTUITION AND EMBRACE THE FIRE WITHIN

Angel Rohrer

Dedicated to Don Jose Ruiz:
In gratitude for leading me to follow the rhythm of my heart.

Hello fierce Warrior.
There you are you glorious being of light.
I've been waiting for you to return home after your epic internal battles.
Come sit by the fire, let me massage your feet and feed you well,
as I know you are only here for a short time
soon you will be out battling our demons once again
I will be here waiting, holding space, always
Love your Goddess.

MY STORY

Nobody escapes Earth unscathed.

Where's a warrior to protect you when you need one?

Oh, you mean I need to be my own warrior? Shit.

Okay, where's a sword and how do I wield this weapon of love?

Know this; you are not alone in your searching for that scathed part of you to be healed, that place where you built so much armor up that you lost connection with your true authentic self, went into survival mode, and picked up a sword to protect yourself.

Picking up that sword, that choice in my mind, was better than dying.

I say that because I found myself in situations over and over again where my life was at risk in the hands of other humans, even the ones who I was supposed to be loved and protected by. I had to leave my natural open state of consciousness to survive, and this caused my tree of life within to suffer in drought.

We are not taught as little ones that we need to learn to protect and save ourselves first. That we have many levels of consciousness we must tend to consistently, to have balance within. *But, if I take care of myself first, isn't that selfish? They will say I am a bitch if I say no to helping them. If I rest, they will call me lazy. If I say "that," I will be abandoned.* We were not taught to hold our inner children's hands, or that we even *have* inner children.

I needed protection in my life, and I was lucky enough to have angels dressed in human skin show up when I needed them. They protected and educated me on how to fight for my life. Their teachings saved my life when I found myself alone, with no protection but my own.

This is the medicine I now share.

When a human finds the balance between their feminine and masculine energy, they step into their channel and connect to the portal they were born to become. When they feel safe, they're then able to attract the life of their dreams. Then and only then, will your divine partner show up to sweep you off your feet, provide a safe space for you to take your beautifully decorated armor off, and lean into the omega, cosmic being you were always meant to be.

Humans are meant to co-create together, so naturally I gravitated towards partners in many shapes and forms, but that one elusive "want" was to be loved by a warrior, a protector, the divine masculine energy I'd been waiting for, the mirror of my dreams. Two humans, both embodying each polarity, allowing for the sacred dance to begin where we could simultaneously hold each other and ourselves.

How did I come to embody this medicine?

It started in 2013, scrolling the good old book of faces:

Wow, what is this? In the Gathering of the Shamans, I recognize that guy from the rehab center I work at; he wrote The 4 Agreements. He's doing a retreat?

All the hairs on my body stood at attention; a wave of dizziness hits me; I close my eyes swallowing hard to diffuse the rising nausea. *Wow, that was intense, perhaps I need to read more about this.*

Reading further, *who are these people and why am I feeling this incredible pull to be there?*

Oh shit, I'd have to travel to Sedona.

Waves of terror rip through my trembling body as tears fall down my cheeks. I close my eyes and travel back to the year 2000 at the World Tumbling and Trampoline Championships in Denmark, where my youngest athlete competed for team Canada. I took the speed train to Copenhagen after the competition by myself at midnight. I made my way to the storage lockers down an empty, long, dark hallway, bent down and unlocked my locker, and pulled my bag out.

As I stood up, the hairs on the back of my neck stood up with me. As I turned around, I was face to face with and surrounded by six surly men. I met the cold hard stare of the man directly in front of me. My stomach went into knots; adrenaline ripped through my body. My higher self chimed in, *Danger! You're in trouble!* As I stood up, I scanned the area for help—no one around. *Shit, okay, let's dance.*

Standing tall, shoulders back, chin up, I got deathly still and breathed deep into my belly; I met and matched his glare with the fire of a dragon: *Do not fuck with me* permeated throughout every inch of my cells. Without breaking our glare, he growled deeply to the men in a different language. The darkness acknowledged and accepted; one slinked forward; it was obvious what their intention was. With actions like those of a feral cat, I escaped, unscathed physically this time, but not emotionally.

My trembling hand found the rail of the dingy, cold escalator. I clung to it, allowing the vibrations to merge with the shaking of my body, urging my spirit back into my body as I rode down to the main area of the train station. I found a security guard standing dutifully by the wall of the station. As my soul found its way back into my body, I found myself behind him—leaning up against the wall behind him, my trembling legs gave away and I slid to the cold, hard ground, urging my shattered heart to stay in my chest.

The security guard slowly turned his head, gazing down upon me with curiosity in his eyes. As our energy connected, my eyes filled with tears and my broken heart started to slow down. He gently smiled and whispered love in Danish which I'm assuming meant, "Are you okay?" I managed a nod; the warrior turned back around, slid his steel toed boot back, connecting his heel with the toes of my shoes and continued his sacred, silent watch.

I was not okay. I heard my husband's voice in my head: *You are leaving your family to traipse across the world for what? Your baby is a year old; you are abandoning her. You aren't even coaching; you don't need to be there; we need you here. This is a huge inconvenience for me!*

My mind provided the reaction it was trained to, supplying the counterpoint to the criticisms; *He will leave me if I tell him this. He will tell me it's my fault again; he now has more confirmation; it's always my fault when men engage me. I will not survive his wrath this time.*

This was the burden I carried, and this story stayed buried deep within, marinating in PTSD, for over a decade.

I popped out of the dream world, opened my moist eyes, and gazed into Don Miguel Ruiz's face on the Facebook event page. So much love, so much magic in this one little picture.

> *It's been years of western medicine and sports philosophies*
> *and I still can't move through these blocks of fear*
> *that keep me held back in my life.*
>
> *Am I really that broken? Really?*
>
> *Perhaps it's time to seek a different modality of healing.*
> *At this point, what do I have to lose?*

I took action and booked the first flight I took by myself in 15 years. Taking action and challenging my fears took me on a grand adventure with a handful of new teachers, new medicine, many vortexes, and magical pyramids.

Five years ago, dreaming at the base of Bell Vortex in Sedona, the download came in on the end of a lightning bolt. No seriously, the thunder and lightning were real, and I stood out in the rain with my arms and heart open wide, singing to the Universe, show me my next step! It was like, right out of a movie, tears and all.

Bring your medicine to the front line, I was told by the Universe.

But how?

I wrangled with this message for the past couple of years while I unraveled my own shadow, sat in many spiritual and recovery circles, and had teachers tell me, "Maybe the message wasn't for you," "You're not special!" as they battled with their own egos.

I chose to dig to the core of my own universe inside, looking for the answers within. I built awareness and leadership programs and took them to a municipality, piloting them in the HR department, with the intent of going within the fire department next. I kept hitting roadblocks navigating with COVID as the war chief. *They weren't ready for me there, or was it that I wasn't ready?* I wrangled this question as the obstacles rose and chose to let go and trust the Universe's plan. I knew in my bones I was being led, I just had to trust and have faith.

My faith was tested once again as my second-year apprenticeship with the Ruiz family was rounding out with a trip to the Teotihuacan pyramids in Mexico in May 2021, which has now become my second home. The COVID war chief struck again with restrictions abounding. *Do I stay and obey the Canadian government rules, or do I trust my fiery intuition burning deep within as I hear the call from Tonantzin?*

Do I challenge my fear of traveling alone once again and get on that plane and honor my truth and intuition, knowing there may also be legal consequences, including huge fines and/or jail time on the other side of this experience from restricted Canadian border crossing? I practiced stillness, breathwork, and deep listening to my body whispering my soul's mission over and over, like a tenacious cat licking you in the same spot—it became painful not to acknowledge the stalking of the jaguar.

Go, my soul whispered as she wrapped her wings around me.
Follow your fire within always, my love.

The sun's rays cascade down my shoulders, sinking and integrating into my cells as I contemplate and journal the morning's experience on the pyramid grounds of Teotihuacan. My jaw clenches as I sense male energy approaching. I take a deep breath, calming my nostril flare at the intrusion of my sacred space as my fingers squeeze my purple pen. "Hi," I choose to shift my body towards him, releasing my pen to the table, and meet his gaze as he respectfully keeps his distance. "I saw you sitting here. We haven't met yet; I'd love to introduce myself if you aren't busy. May I join you?"

As our eyes connect, blinding energy fills our space; time and words fly as six hours turn into recovering lifetimes of soul fragments. "You are a fire captain from Washington State? No way! How is this possible?" I shook my head in disbelief as I gazed into this human's piercing blue eyes, clear as day, and the storyline drops in like a bomb exploding into our timeline.

Nine months later, literally a human birthing process on this Earth, we were formally united in marriage and mission. Presiding over the ceremony was a holistic healer, while one of his beloved crew members in the fire department served as our witness and best man.

Re-birth can be messy. It can also be glorious. It can also be both. There is magic in holding them both, holding duality as we walk with one foot in one dimension and the other foot connected to the Divine. Holding and loving both transmit you to a whole other dimension.

When you set your intent, when you want to manifest something in your life, you don't always know how it will show up, but when you're open and willing to surrender and receive, magic happens.

This part we are at now is easy.

Getting to this part took copious amounts of courage and action. The Toltecs call this process of awareness, Jaguar Medicine. I made a conscious choice to be the cycle breaker of my family. I made a conscious choice to break my own agreements and societies' agreements around what it means to be a human right now during this most precarious time on Earth.

Are you ready to make some conscious agreements yourself?

Are you ready to learn and integrate Jaguar Medicine and manifest the life of your dreams?

Don't say yes to me. Say yes to yourself. Commit to yourself.

THE PRACTICE

This is the work of a warrior—using ruthless love against the darkness held within.

We're taught to love and give attention to our strengths, and through this process I've learned we need to love and give more attention to our weaknesses with all that we have. This is how we heal.

This is how we release our feral, traumatized inner children from their cages.

We heal by accepting all of us, just the way we are.

This allows us to love and accept others just the way they are.

To start healing, we need to first start with a "check-in" point. How can we build a new storyline for ourselves or know where to go for help if we don't first identify where we need to start?

Allow the ruthless love to come in.

It's time to own where you are in this timeline of your life. Knowing if you're lying about where you are, the only person you're lying to is yourself. This work is deeply personal and demands 100 percent responsibility from you. You can't be a clean mirror for others if you won't clean your own mirror.

In other words, you can't expect authenticity from another human when you can't be authentic with yourself. Owning where you are along your journey will create powerful transformation.

This process of "owning where you are" is a practice, and at the beginning of your process, you will need to do it a lot. The Universe can't make you a framework if you're lying to yourself about where you are in your process. It would be like going to a university-level calculus class and trying to enter with elementary-level math knowledge. You'll be spinning in no time or be shown the door.

It's okay to be in elementary school. Our inner children live there. If you reject the thought of starting over or going back in time, you're rejecting the part of you that experienced that timeline. Chances are, they need you desperately right now. See yourself beginning this project with creativity and an opportunity to play.

Can you own where you are in your storyline? Can you be the author of your story? Can you make the necessary changes to create the life you want to live? No judgment.

Understand, you're building a framework for this new storyline you are creating.

STEP 1: M.E.P.S.S

Get a journal and answer the following questions.

Where are you?

- Where are you mentally?
- Where are you emotionally?
- Where are you physically?
- Where are you spiritually?
- Where are you socially?

Self-rejection and self-sabotage are things to watch out for. Understand most of the work will come from staying with yourself as you work through these layers. This is where we choose to show up for our inner children and be the parents we needed back then. You get to be your own parent. Yay!

Why is this exciting? Because you are the only one who knows deeply what your inner child needs, as you are the only one who has experienced life your way! Everyone is dreaming their own dream. It's time for you to take 100 percent responsibility for your storyline and heal the pieces keeping you stuck.

Where are you stuck? It's time to go on an adventure to find out!

STEP 2: ACCOUNTABILITY WITH YOURSELF

You, as your greatest and most powerful teacher, will be the one you're checking in with in the beginning. After you're finished writing down where you are in each branch, take your list and go find a mirror.

Take a couple of minutes to connect with yourself in the mirror.

Then read your list to yourself in the mirror. Engage with yourself as you would another beloved; coach yourself as you would someone else; cheerlead yourself in the places you are succeeding and bring love and support to the places where you need it.

STEP 3: ASK FOR HELP

Be honest with yourself and own it if you don't have any other ideas to shift your blocks. Promise yourself you'll find the right humans to assist you with the parts you're struggling with, and acknowledge you aren't going anywhere and will be with yourself each step of the way.

STEP 4: TRAIN YOUR WARRIOR TO STAND WATCH

This is the most important part of the process; never abandon yourself.

Be your own warrior. Stand up for yourself when your inner child needs it, and if you are both in over your head, ask for help. Be open to accepting the help.

Choose you, always. When you start to feel overwhelmed or the anxiety creeps back in, go back to the beginning: "Where are you mentally?" Go through the process again.

Consistency wins every time. Consistency builds trust within yourself.

Prove to yourself you can show up and be present for yourself. Put in the reps.

The warrior's ruthless love shows up and is present, for yourself, first.

Show up for yourself first. Be 100 percent responsible for your storyline, and take action and you'll witness the entire Universe conspire to give you the life of your dreams.

STEP 5: TAKE ACTION

After you finish the exercise, I'm right here if you need a consult for your next steps.

Check out my bio for where and how to connect with me and understand, I'm already proud of you for getting this far already, and so is your goddess within.

It's big work to commit to holding your inner child's hand, healing yourself, and asking for help along the way!

"Help me to heal the world, starting with healing yourself first."

~ Don Miguel Ruiz

#goteam
#lovewarriors

Angel Rohrer is a former high-performance coach in the power tumbling and trampoline world. She comes with 25 years of National level experience training athletes of all ages and genders. After retiring, the last ten years were spent focusing her coaching skills in the holistic community, becoming a Crystal Reiki Master teacher and deep tissue massage specialist. She began coaching and healing those looking to wrangle their shadows of life, as well as healing their physical body.

Ancient medicine has always been a calling and she spent 30 years mastering breathwork and moving energy with Kung Fu martial arts, as well as apprenticing with the Ruiz family (Author of *The 4 Agreements*), Toltec Shamans of the Eagle Knight lineage over the last three years.

She holds hands with the Angel of Death and knows how to navigate darkness with her unique ray of light holding the element of transformation in her soul.

She will commit to you

as deep as you will commit to your own transformation,

walk beside you

as you take that first step into the fire,

so you can shine

your brilliant ray of light.

This is her mission.

Connect with Angel:

Website: https://www.angelrohrer.com

Facebook: https://www.facebook.com/angelrohrer444

Instagram: https://www.instagram.com/angel.rohrer/

TikTok: https://www.tiktok.com/@angel.rohrer?lang=en

Stay tuned for her new book being released later this year, *A Walk with Jaguar*. A fierce truth about shadow work and transformation.

*"Your will requires your discipline as you master
a new way of life."*

~ Angel Rohrer

CHAPTER 10

THE JOURNEY TO AUTHENTIC LOVE
HOW WE SHOW UP FOR ONE IS HOW WE SHOW UP FOR ALL

Carolyn McGee, Decision Queen,
Sacred Haven Living and Intuition Expert

MY STORY

I felt a piece of me shrink and want to hide.

When do I get to be done with people taking their insecurities, fears, and lack of personal growth out on me? Yet another friend was not seeing my value or contribution and was accusing me of not giving enough. I tried my best not to take it personally, but it felt personal. Over the years I developed a habit of not setting good boundaries and being afraid to speak my truth. Even in this relationship, I could look back and see times when there had been untrue comments that I didn't call out because I didn't want to rock the boat. I let them slide, and by not advocating for me, made things worse because I didn't speak up.

There were times when I was treated differently than others in our friendship circle. I was held to a different standard. This was a long-term pattern for me. When I was a child, I had to take care of my younger sister and I developed a pattern of putting everyone else's needs before mine. This pattern showed up in every area of my life.

I let friends borrow money when I was in debt, I said yes to projects and events even when I was full with my own commitments, and I took care of friends' kids, but never asked for help with mine. I sacrificed my health to support others.

I didn't love myself enough to say no, ask, and receive.

This was the universe giving me an opportunity to say: *"No, thank you. I'm done with this pattern."* But to do that, I would have to be vulnerable. *Speaking my truth might end the relationship. Am I okay with that?* Was I ready to let go and let this other person decide? *Do they value our relationship enough to acknowledge their part in what isn't working?*

One of my favorite healing tools is Ho'oponopono. The concept that we all own part of our experiences is intriguing. The other person might be 99% wrong, but we own our 1% of the problem. It's simply accepting responsibility for our contribution. When others don't own their contribution, the relationship will never be successful, no matter how hard I try to fix it. I must own my part and accept that if the other doesn't, then it may be time to let go.

One of my big learning opportunities was my relationship with my ex-husband and understanding the disconnect between what we each needed to feel loved and successful. He needed to win, to be right. I needed the energy of win-win and compromise. These are radically different approaches which cannot be successful together.

Once I realized that since his version of love is "power over," instead of finding a path to agreement, I knew we couldn't heal and grow together. *I can't be in a relationship with someone who doesn't take any responsibility.* That's not love. That's acting out as the small, wounded child, trying to make yourself feel better.

This was my childhood pattern of "I wasn't good enough" or "I didn't try hard enough." Launching deeper into personal healing, creating healthy boundaries, and acknowledging how each person has a contribution and responsibility for a healthy relationship creates a beautiful balance of accountability.

Unfortunately, my friend chose not to work on our relationship. My heart hurt at a loss, but I realized she was never a true friend to start with because of the way she treated me and the fact that she couldn't see who I was. She only saw what she needed me to be.

That realization opened more flow in my business. It allowed me to release the thought that I needed to be perfect, and that other people's opinions matter more than mine. Stepping into being my own love warrior by loving myself and setting boundaries felt easier. Each time I said, "No," each time I said, "Could you please explain that again? I don't understand what you're saying to me," or "I don't see things that way," strengthened my own sense of purpose.

I began to love all aspects of myself and realized that if someone can't accept me as me, that's their loss. Then I was able to make new friends, create new opportunities, and expand my business. New healthy relationships developed that were more balanced, nurtured me, and allowed me to nurture them. It was easy. I felt safe asking for help and offering help. It was balanced. And that's what true love really is. It's stepping into giving and receiving on both sides—being able to receive as well as give. When we only give, often there's an underlying energy of anticipation of getting something back. This hidden string of expectations is not truly giving.

This opened all my energy. It allowed me to show up bigger and better. My intuition expanded, better relationships came into play, and more opportunities showed up.

I had another opportunity to work on the pattern when I started my intuition business while my pet business continued to thrive. The pet business was easier because, in my mind, it was conventional. Even though I was one of the first pet businesses to open in my area, it was still an understood business. You walk dogs and scoop litter boxes. But talking to angels and animals, and doing energy work and healing? Hmm. That required a whole different level of openness and transparency.

It was challenging for me to let clients and acquaintances who knew me as a pet care business owner know my additional gifts. I feared losing existing business if I opened to what else I offered. When a cat owner said, "Fluffy is not using her litter box. While we are away, let us know if you notice anything wrong." I telepathically saw the cat stepping into the box and the cover falling off, scaring the cat to eliminate just outside the box. Instead of telling the truth and helping the client connect deeper to the cat, I said, "I noticed the litter box cover is cracked and doesn't fit well. It was next to the box when Fluffy didn't use it. Perhaps you should replace it."

I missed an opportunity to be authentic and provide more value to my client. My fear of "it isn't safe to be me" impacted my energy and blocked me from being of greater service to my clients.

This energy of feeling like I couldn't be open to who I truly am, decreased my visibility. I stopped my regular emails and showing up on social media, hiding instead of being vulnerable. It was only when I started doing *Evolutionary Mystic Meditation* and Inner Child Trauma work that I realized I was just protecting the little child, this small aspect of me that held my hurts.

The last layer was working on the trauma healing, seeing the patterns of behavior that stemmed from an initial wounding. As I released these patterns, and started to truly love myself unconditionally, I could release any anger and resentment towards people who hurt me.

As I got to know this part of me that wanted to be safe and joyful, and seen as who she is, I started feeling safer as the adult learning how to love and protect this aspect of me. Speaking to and loving my inner child as I did my own children nurtured all parts of me.

Asking my inner child, "What do you need today?" connected all aspects of me. Her favorite way to engage is playing in nature. Nestled in a hammock swing hanging from a tree in my yard, feeling the breeze on my skin, hearing the birds chirp with the sun filtering through the leaves brings her joy, and she whispers, "I am safe—you are safe—we are safe to be seen."

Embracing the love and joy of my inner child provided energy and clarity to be more transparent, reach out to my friends when I was struggling a little bit, and even let my children know when I was having a hard time. I shared all my gifts with my pet business clients. It made such a profound difference in my mental, spiritual, emotional, and physical health.

I started being more authentic. I wasn't sharing all my trials and tribulations, but being genuine. If something didn't work, I said it. When I was struggling with trying to figure out what my niche was, I asked questions, "Hey, how do you see me when you think of me?" The answers filled my heart with joy. I realized how much love and respect I had for being me and not being perfect.

This completely changed the way I showed up in life, in all my relationships, especially in my business. I truly became a beacon of authentic and unconditional love.

The more I loved that little girl, the more she loved me back, and the safer we both felt to be out in the world and be seen.

I remember the first time an internet troll commented on one of my videos. In the past I would've cried and probably taken the video down. In this case, I remembered what one of my teachers said, "Carolyn, when you get a troll commenting, it means you've made it. Celebrate that!" And so, I did, I stood up in my office and I danced, and I thanked the troll for making the comment. I knew I was being seen as the beacon of light that I am, the path of light and love.

There were no strings attached to any relationships anymore. If I felt someone setting the expectation of "I give, and you owe me," I was able to feel it, see it, detach it, and clarify the expectation. "I appreciate your help. Are you expecting anything in return?" "I would love to speak at your event. Do you need anything from me?" This gave people the opportunity to consciously look at their expectations. "I didn't realize that I was expecting you to know what I needed." They didn't even realize they were doing it. It was a gift for both of us, for me to be able to acknowledge what I was seeing and ask, "How can we make our relationship more authentic, open, and balanced?" Some people walked away, but most were grateful.

My next step in my healing was to truly experience the divine masculine and divine feminine energy. The divine masculine was the "action taking" and "producing" energy I developed in my pet business. I excelled in that arena. I now got to explore and embrace the divine feminine—the divine feminine energy of unconditional love, creation, and nurturing our energy from a spiritual aspect.

I started to envision this mother energy holding my little child and just loving on her, and it cemented my transformation. The more time I spent loving this small part of me, the healthier all my relationships became.

My gift to you is to take you on a healing journey with your divine feminine mother and your little child to help you be seen as your beautiful, bright, authentic soul.

If after reading my chapter and practice, you are curious about how you can connect deeper to your inner child, divine guidance, and intuition, to trust it and take action without second guessing, I invite you to find a time to chat with me. https://CarolynMcGee.as.me/VirtualCoffee

THE PRACTICE

Sit in a comfortable chair with your feet on the ground or sit directly on the ground. Keep your spine straight.

Take three deep breaths in through your nose and out through your mouth.

Imagine you're in a bubble of energy, like a soap bubble that surrounds your body. If there is any energy that's not yours, or is not of love, ask it to leave. Call back any energy of yours that was left with other people or events. Envision a blue light surrounding the bubble, protecting you and your energy.

Focus on the energy of your heart chakra—the spot in the center of your chest.

Imagine a pillar of white light that starts in your heart and extends past your throat through your head and out the top of your head into your own personal star, 36 inches above your head. This is your connection to the divine masculine, the source of spiritual guidance and inspiration.

Now bring your awareness back to your heart and see that pillar of white light extend from your heart, past your belly, and through your hips out of your body into the Earth. Feel that pillar of light moving down into the center of Mother Earth. This is your connection to the divine feminine.

Feel the energy move through your divine heart, connecting you to the divine feminine and the divine masculine, your connection to all that is and all that ever will be.

1. Imagine a loving, kind, maternal energy, an energy of pure, unconditional love. This energy is all knowing, all caring, and loves all life equally. This energy, which I call the divine mother, is the divine feminine at her essence. All life is born through her. All creativity, abundance, nurturing—everything around us—came from this beautiful energy. And this energy is unconditional. It sees the positive in all, and sees the spark of divinity in our souls and in our hearts. There is no judgment or comparison. We are all loved.

2. Hold the vision of this divine feminine energy, and bring into your awareness that vulnerable child, the piece of you that's been hurt in the past. You may call it your inner child or your wounded child,

but just see this beautiful aspect of yourself who has been hurt over the years, not allowed to fully develop or step into their full purpose. This aspect of yourself has held the pain for all the other parts of yourself so that they could grow and thrive while this small aspect suffers.

3. I invite you to ask this divine mother, this divine feminine aspect, if she would unconditionally love this inner child and see her entire face glow. She is so thrilled with the opportunity to love one of her children. Envision her opening her arms and inviting this small child to come into her lap, to be held, nurtured, and seen through the eyes of the divine. Imagine your small child being held and loved as they have never been before. See that child be happy and safe to take that chance to be vulnerable and climb up into the lap of this divine mother. And then see the child's body start to relax, see the child starting to feel safe.

4. See the child look up into the divine feminine eyes and see your child's divinity reflected back. This is the unconditional love of the Creator, the mother of us all. Allow that child to feel loved, not held back, but supported, nurtured, cared for, and totally seen— seen for their own beautiful attributes, for who they are at their essence. As you witness this, feel your own physical body start to relax even more.

5. When the child is ready, full of divine love and full of self-respect, worthy, ready to be seen, and ready to go out into the world and be herself, then ask the child to give the divine mother one more hug and step down off of her lap and fade away. Thank the divine mother for the unconditional love she always provides, specifically for loving this one child. Then allow her energy to fade away.

Start to bring your awareness back into this time and space.

I would love to hear how your life changes as you embrace your inner child. Do you have more energy? Is it easier for you to show up authentically? Do you love and accept yourself and others more?

If you prefer to listen to the meditation, I have a recording on my website. You can download it and other gifts at https://carolynmcgee.com/resources/

You may also email me at carolyn@carolynmcgee.com with any questions, comments, or observations.

Carolyn McGee is the founder of Sacred Haven Living, a community where you learn to heal using life's experiences. Her values are community, connection, and collaboration. She thrives on helping women break patterns to understand their relationship with themselves, others, money, and spirit.

As the Decision Queen, she guides you to trust your intuition to make empowered decisions without second guessing to take inspired action! She has taught thousands of women to trust themselves and their intuition so they can show up in their full power in business and life.

With a background of 20+ years in high tech, Carolyn knows firsthand the importance of living from a blend of her masculine and feminine energies to take authentic and heart-centered actions.

She is the lead author of the #1 bestselling book, *Inspired Living: Superpowers for Health, Love and Business,* and she has co-authored 15+ bestselling books, is a popular TV co-host, and sought-after speaker and blogger.

https://www.amazon.com/Inspired-Living-Superpowers-Health-Business-ebook/dp/B0B674RTRK

To learn more about Carolyn, or to contact her, visit
https://www.CarolynMcGee.com

You can join her Inspired Living Community:
https://www.facebook.com/groups/inspiredlivingsuperpowerscommunity/

Find out about her latest workshops:
https://carolynmcgee.com/workshops/

Like her Facebook page:
https://www.facebook.com/CarolynMcgeeIntuitiveCoach/

Experience tools from other books and classes:
https://www.CarolynMcGee.com/resources

Get Carolyn's free Intuition gift:
https://carolynmcgee.com/soul-clarity-gift/

"Living your best inspired life includes recognizing, embracing, and sharing all your superpowers."

~ Carolyn McGee

CHAPTER 11

STANDING IN THE SPOTLIGHT
RELEASE YOUR FEAR. SHARE YOUR LIGHT.
MAKE YOUR UNIQUE IMPACT.

Ginny Robertson

MY STORY

"Thanks for asking," I said. "But I don't do that. It's not my thing."

"It's not a request," he replied. "You're doing it!"

His words startled me, and I felt fear rising from my gut. My typical response came easily because I'd been practicing it for 30 years. This was the first time it was met with resistance. Something else was also happening for the first time: I had the thought, *How do I know I don't do it and that it's not my thing when I've never done it before?*

This scene between my employer and my 35-year-old-self played out the week before I was to attend a conference in New York City. He received a call that one of the speakers canceled and was asked to recommend a replacement. I was the replacement.

The puzzled look on his face told me he couldn't understand why I wasn't excited and jumping at the opportunity. The puzzled look on my face had nothing to do with him and everything to do with what was happening inside me. My fear was being overridden by curiosity. *How do I know I don't do it and that it's not my thing when I've never done it before?*

I worked in the banking industry and was recently promoted to Assistant Vice President. The conference was a national gathering of thousands of industry professionals, and now I would be speaking to them. While I doubt I'd have been fired for refusing, it wouldn't have boded well for my career. And, as I mentioned, there was this demanding curiosity bubbling up inside, and I had to respond to it.

The fear didn't go away, but I knew my stuff and was well-prepared. I did okay.

But the outcome isn't the story here. The story is what was shifting inside.

A TIME OF CHANGE

This happened during a time of painful personal changes, disruption, turmoil, and significant growth. I went through a divorce, had a demanding, often stressful job with a killer daily commute, and was trying to be a *perfect* mother to my eight-year-old son. I was also in therapy and doing other personal growth work that was kicking my butt.

A lot was opening inside of me, and I think that's why, for the first time, I was more curious than fearful about speaking in public. The question of *how do I know* was front and center. Something had also been jarred loose, a memory from childhood.

THE MEMORY

It's Easter Sunday, and my mother, father, and I arrive early as my father has responsibilities before church. My Sunday school teacher tells me, "Our class is doing a pageant for the church. I gave the roles out last Sunday so everyone could memorize their part. You weren't here, but I'd like you to participate, so here's a poem for you to read."

My seven-year-old precocious self thinks, *I will not be the only kid who doesn't know their part. I'm great at memorizing. I can do this!*

It's my turn. I confidently leave the copy of the poem in my seat and walk to the front, quite full of myself. I love my new Easter dress, bonnet, white patent leather shoes, and little lacy umbrella purse. I look out over the crowded room and begin to recite. And then my brain goes blank, and I don't remember what comes next. I'm trying so hard to think of the next line, but it isn't coming, and the silence in the church is deafening. All these people are looking at me, and now I'm frightened. *Oh no! I'm going to have to go sit down in defeat.*

Someone in the congregation laughs, and I bolt. I run down the aisle and out the door. I throw myself to the ground hiding under the sagging limbs of a weeping willow tree. My mother comes out and tries to console me, but I'm inconsolable, and I refuse to go back to the church. I stay outside alone with my sorrow until the service is over.

People are leaving the church, so I get on my feet and stand near my parents. Their friends say, "I felt so bad for her," and "It really was cute." I think *I just want to get out of here. It wasn't cute. It was embarrassing. Why did that guy laugh at me? Doesn't he know that's hurtful?*

The only thing I remember my parents saying after that is, "It's okay," and "No one will remember it next week."

While I did not consciously remember that experience (until I did), the memory and feelings of humiliation were real and stored in my body. They were running the show.

WHAT CAME BEFORE

As a small child, I was pretty full of myself. All it took was another person in the room for me to go into entertainment mode. Memories of my three-year-old self included strumming my toy ukulele and singing and dancing with joy and abandonment. I was happy to be the center of attention.

WHAT CAME AFTER

Within a year or two of my experience at church, my mother started calling me out for showing off and always wanting to be the center of attention. It was a confusing time because she had laughed and sometimes danced with me in the past. Now the rules had changed, and it wasn't cute anymore, and I didn't know why. I was supposed to be polite and quiet and only speak when spoken to by adults—seen and not heard. My mother said, "Don't brag about your accomplishments because it might make someone who isn't as accomplished feel bad." I was also learning that my mother preferred calm, polite Ginny to full-of-herself Ginny. Her love started to feel conditional, and I learned to play the game at a young age.

Part of me shut down. I learned to read the energy of our home and know just what to do to ensure my mother was okay with me. I became a chameleon who could easily adjust to others' expectations, and a *good girl* was born. I would get glimpses of a higher, wiser self, and even as a kid, I knew I was playing a game and that this wasn't the *real* me.

To be clear, I wasn't shy or timid. I still felt bold in some situations. I was a leader in high school. In fact, I was the President of the Thespians Club, an acting organization. I would often get asked why I didn't try out for a play or similar opportunity; guess what I'd say? *I don't do that. It's not my thing.* I did well in a required speech class because I could read my speech. The unconscious fear of forgetting what I was going to say and the ensuing humiliation were removed. I ran for and won a student government seat during my freshman year in college and continued to lead in other ways. I had a successful career in corporate finance and loved managing and mentoring my staff.

But something was missing. An essential part of me wasn't showing up fully. Remembering the speaking story shook me out of my unconscious fear of being humiliated. But something much bigger was going on.

This wasn't about speaking or humiliation at all.

It was about my fear of being *too big* or *too much*. In my child's mind, there were prices for being that *full of myself* little girl. The adult woman knew those prices were too big to pay and that they outweighed any false feelings of safety and security she got from playing small.

I mentioned earlier that during that time of change, I was doing some personal growth work that was kicking my butt. Less than a year after that speaking gig in New York City, that company invited me into their facilitator training program. I was ready and said yes. I left my corporate job a year later to work for them full-time. A few years later, I went out on my own, and I haven't looked back.

My fear kept me out of the spotlight. Had I not interrupted that pattern, I could have easily missed opportunities that place me right here, delightfully living my purpose.

WHAT ABOUT YOU?

Do you yearn to be in the spotlight? To teach, show, mentor, and influence? Is there an impact you know is yours to make? What might be getting in your way of stepping out and being seen and heard?

I love the word spotlight. It can mean to *be illuminated* (to be in the spotlight), and it can also mean to *be the illuminator* (to shine a spotlight on). Does that word feel too big for you? If so, remember that the spotlight is where you shine and where you can make your most significant impact. The size of the spotlight or the audience isn't what's most important. Most important is that you shine your light in the direction of those you are here to help.

DO YOU DESIRE TO:

Teach what you know and support others to heal?

Make a difference in a small circle or lead a large group?

Network in a way that feels good to you and lets your light shine?

Write a blog, an article, or a book?

Counsel or coach one-on-one or speak from a stage to thousands?

Be interviewed or be the interviewer on a podcast?

Teach art one-on-one or have a gallery show?

Run for political office or work for a political campaign?

Be of service in your unique way?

Whether you coach one-on-one or speak on a stage to thousands, you must free yourself from those old (sometimes ancient, primarily unconscious) fears holding you back. How do you gain clarity and interrupt the pattern that keeps you from stepping into the spotlight? Here is what helped me.

THE PRACTICE

How I got from there to here, and how you can too.

THE CYCLE

You've had experiences.

Experiences create memories.

Memories create beliefs.

Beliefs create an identity.

Identity creates a thought.

Thought creates a feeling.

From that feeling, you take action.

From that action, you get a result.

A RESULT YOU DON'T LIKE

When you get a result you don't like, what do you typically do to try and fix it? There's a good chance you'll return to that action step. If you just *do* something different, you'll get a different result. Right?

Let's say you're a budding entrepreneur with a service that excites you and you believe is needed. You feel confident about what you're offering, have a website, develop a list of interested people, and know that you must get out there and talk about what you do. You're comfortable thinking about your business and excited about working with and helping your ideal clients. But you panic when you think about getting out there and being seen and heard in a more significant way. Or maybe you've known for some time that you have a book in you because you know things that could benefit others. You're excited about having a book but not enthusiastic about writing because *you're not a writer.*

WHAT IF?

What if, instead of *doing something different,* like forcing yourself to show up when you know you're not ready, you ask yourself, *how do I feel about being more visible?* What if, instead of trying to start that book when deep inside you believe you're not a writer, you ask yourself, *how do I know*

I'm not a writer? This can be an exciting time of excavation, where you uncover what's beneath the belief.

USING MY CHILDHOOD EXPERIENCE WITH MY MOTHER, HERE'S THE CYCLE THAT PLAYED OUT FOR ME.

My Experience: I'm told it's not okay to be the center of attention anymore and to stop showing off.

My Memory: My mother was unhappy with my behavior when I showed up too big.

My Belief: If I continue to show up that way, my mother will be displeased and withhold love.

My Identity: I'm a good girl.

My Thought: I clearly know good girl behavior and must conform.

My Feeling: It's not safe to step out of line.

My Action: I behave in a way I believe others expect. I don't promote myself. I stay out of the spotlight.

My Result: I miss opportunities and experiences to grow and shine.

To shift from non-speaker to speaker, I had to interrupt the pattern in the gap between identity and thought. When I asked myself, *how do I know I don't do that? I've never done it.* I moved from habitual thinking and embraced new opportunities and possibilities. To shift from good girl to potential badass, I had to interrupt the pattern of good girl thinking and begin to believe that it is safe to be bold in the world. I understood that the price I paid for playing small was greater than my fear of playing big.

YOUR TURN

If you've read this far, you're probably attracted to the spotlight, but maybe you don't know what standing in it looks like. Or you're already comfortable in the spotlight and want more of it.

Think about something you yearn to do in a more significant way that will put you in the spotlight.

What is it that I want to do?

Why do I want to do it?

Who benefits when I do it?

What are some fears that keep me from doing it?

What are some prices I have paid for not doing it?

Am I going to do it anyway?

SOMEONE WHO BELIEVES THAT BEING A WRITER IS *NOT THEIR THING* MIGHT ANSWER THIS WAY:

I want to write a book because I have wisdom and knowledge to share to help others heal. I have fear about not being a good writer, so I either won't finish the book, or it won't be worthy. One price I've paid for not doing it is that I don't get to share what I believe I'm here to do, which hurts my soul. I will do it anyway because the price I'm paying that hurts my soul is much higher than my fear of not being good enough.

Using **the cycle** below, tap into a memory of an experience that might keep you from taking that step you say you want to take. Perhaps a teacher or other authority figure labeled you a *poor writer. Take that experience and go through the steps below until you get to the result:*

I want to write, but I don't.

My Experience:

My Memory:

My Belief:

My Identity:

My Thought:

My Feeling:

My Action:

My Result:

This is not a one-and-done process. Take quiet time and sit with these questions and your answers often and see what bubbles to the surface. These steps can help you understand how you got to *your result.* Then, go through each step again, find where you can interrupt the pattern, make new choices, and you're on your way.

I'll see you in the spotlight!

TWO INVITATIONS:

Take my "Are You Ready For the Spotlight?"
Quiz: https://opwgc.com/spotlight/

Reach out if you feel stuck or have questions about the process. I'd love to hear from you. ginnyrobertsonopw@gmail.com

Ginny Robertson *connects women around the world to their gifts, their purpose, and each other.* She supports women with opportunities for deep connection, more visibility, and being comfortable playing a more significant role on the planet. She shines a light on and supports women in being seen and heard in more meaningful ways, creating opportunities for them to share their gifts and make a unique difference.

Ginny offers these opportunities in three ways:

On Purpose Woman Global Community - founded in 2000. Ginny held in-person gatherings in Maryland and Virginia. In 2020, because of COVID, she took everything online and created a global community. She invites all women who yearn for deeper connection and more visibility to try one of our many free monthly online gatherings. There are also in-person gatherings in Maryland, Virginia, and Florida.

On Purpose Woman Online Magazine - founded in 2003. On Purpose Woman Magazine was a free print magazine for 12 years. After taking a break, Ginny shifted to an online magazine accessible to everyone. It is a perfect place for women to find information and resources for their minds, their bodies, their spirits, and their Businesses.

Real Women Real Purpose Talk Show - Ginny is the co-host. She talks with women living on purpose, sharing their gifts, and making their unique difference.

Ginny is an inspirational speaker, workshop facilitator, author and was the co-host of WomanTalk Live radio show on WCBM in Baltimore. In 2012, she was named one of Maryland's Top 100 Women by The Daily Record, Maryland's premier business, law, and government newspaper.

Ginny lives in Maryland with her soulmate, Don. She loves live music, especially classic rock, the ocean, the mountains, and deep connections.

Connect with Ginny:

Website: https://www.opwgc.com

YouTube:
https://www.youtube.com/c/OnPurposeWomanGlobalCommunity

Email: ginnyrobertsonopw@gmail.com

"To shift from good girl to potential badass, I had to interrupt the pattern of good girl thinking and begin to believe it was safe to be bold in the world. I understood that the price I paid for playing small was greater than my fear of playing big."

~ Ginny Robertson

CHAPTER 12

A HIGHER VIBRATION
HOW TO EMBODY THE FREQUENCY OF LOVE

Sharon Josef, Ph.D., Channeler, Medical Intuitive

MY STORY

When Laura Di Franco (the publisher of this and other amazing books) invited me to collaborate on the *Love Warriors* book, I thought to myself: *How can love go with **war(rior)**?* The more I felt into it, the more I got it: Being a warrior means to champion, advocate, be a guardian, a supporter of, or rally for, not necessarily to "fight" for. Although if "fight" didn't have the heaviness that comes with it, I'd definitely fight for it, because love is everything to me.

When one writes in a book, it's usually telling a story unless it's a "how to" book. I'm very tempted to write the how-to of love. I worked very hard at releasing all the drama and trauma of my life, so I prefer to make up new and better stories as I go forward, and what can be better than love?

I'll write the how-to of love later in this chapter because, as my guides pointed out, we really do not know-comprehend-practice true love. We know to say "unconditional love," but it's one thing to say it, and another to practice and be that. The closest to unconditional we get is with our children. However, even with our children, we act from our subconscious and conditioned patterns. For example: "If you don't listen to me you will not. . ." or, "You're a good boy/ girl. . ." because they follow our instructions, or behave in a certain way.

You can see that there's no unconditional love here (on Earth at this time) right now. Perhaps a few do know how to hold that frequency and practice it as much as they can, but they're few and far between.

I started by promising myself that I would allow my kids to be who they truly are, without putting any of my agenda in place. For most of their life, I've done that; however, I'm sure there were some interferences where I wanted to protect them, or I thought it was my duty as a mom to inform them of this or that. In truth, they have their own journey to follow. Their - and your - soul knows how to lead you down a path that is right for them, and for you. There is no need for anyone to interfere. The interference is when fear takes the place of love.

Before I write what the guides said about love, I'll tell you a story. This is a love I have with my husband of many years. We started out being on the same page. Before we married we had a serious conversation about many subjects, but the most important to me was to share my outlook on life, that all is, and comes from Spirit. This is the vantage point I live my life from. "Spirituality is a big part of my life. It gives my life meaning! Would you take part in my explorations of it?" To that my husband replied: "Let's start our day by meditating together." We did a lot together as a young couple. I declared that we were pretty much equal partners and it went well. However, as we started our married life, I took on these old patterns of the wife putting her husband and children first. I didn't listen to my inner voice: *What is it that you really want? Why are you sad? Are you living from a place of what your essence is like—who you really are and strive to be?* Until such time, I didn't even know what it was I wanted for myself. I was quite miserable for a while when my kids were very young and my husband worked long hours.

It took me many years and deep digging to find myself again. I needed to do it so I could find my joy. At the time, I was more interested in helping people professionally, so my guides told me: *You cannot do it without clearing and cleaning all your old patterns and belief systems.*

I want to add that it's so very hard to get rid of old patterns. There are the ancestral ones that we took on to clear for everyone—mine was to stay small. With that was the challenge to speak out and feel confident to be in my truth. This is a work in progress. It goes in spirals. We keep clearing it and then we sail around and meet it on a deeper level until it does not show up again in our life. Then there are the patterns we took on from our past lives or our childhood traumas. We usually bring a different story to this life that addresses the same lesson we had from the other lifetimes. It's so easy for me to see it on my clients and friends, but not as easy to look at my stories. I can see my past lives, and I do see the patterns that keep showing up for me, but there is a time when we feel ready to tackle things. Even though we know our stories, we are not always ready to make the right connection to our life, nor are we ready to take the steps to change things immediately, even if we know what we want.

The more I got into spiritual work; the more my husband got out of it. I learned to really accept him and other family members and friends where they were at— awareness-wise, or whatever their belief system is. I remember asking my guides about certain family members, saying to them: *I always hear the same stories and they talk about the same subjects; I don't want to do it anymore. I have no stimulation or anything.*

My guides said: *Connect in the love, and you will see them and the world differently!*

I would like to share with you that my husband and I have gone through a few chapters in our love together. It has been joyful, but also a lot of work. It has been hard to release the conditioning of "you should do this for me" or "I should be doing that for him." Should is not a word we want to be using in love. Nor should anyone's partner be a martyr or a victim. Wouldn't it be so easy if we accepted each other wherever we are, how we are? No judgment, only simple giving and receiving? When there are no expectations there are no disappointments.

I learned to look deep within when I have a complaint. What do I need from him means to me: *How can I get this on my own? Or, what button is it pushing inside and why?* It isn't because partners aren't meant to help each other. But only because when I'm needy, it's something inside of me I want to work on. Changing my inner landscape shows up in the outer world.

The way we've been conditioned to think and act for many eons is to treat or think of love as an emotion. This is the reason we have conditions: *If you do this for me I will appreciate you more, or I will know that you love me.* For kids: "If you behave this way, you're a good boy/girl." We come into this life experience knowing our worth and loving ourselves, but then our environment (parents, teachers, friends) teaches us conditional love.

We seek approval in our partner's eyes or opinion, or we feel what we do or who we are is not enough. If the general consensus is that one is pretty if she is skinny or has big boobs, or is small chested and rounded, or whatever most buy into it. Why is it that we don't hold into the knowing that we're worthy by being part of God-Goddess-All that is? We are a spark of the Divine. As such, we are whole and complete; we are worthy! We do not need to seek our worthiness in our parents' eyes, not in our partner's eyes, nor in our eyes. We feel we're not pretty or handsome enough, not smart or educated enough, not rich enough, etc.—simply not enough.

Each of us has one strong sentence that represents us. For me it was (and still is at times): *I don't do enough.* I don't think I was consciously aware of it, nor can I say how I picked up this way of being. The outcome was that I always spread myself thin by doing too much for other people. The story I told myself was: *I have these gifts to help others, so I need to use them to help* at the expense of overdoing it. Most of the time I was exhausted, and every once in a while, I collapsed energetically. At that point I couldn't even communicate with my closest friends, not to mention my clients. I ended up hurting so many of my friends and family members when I was exhausted like that.

I also told myself: *I get bored with doing just one thing. I need to do a variety of things at the same time to feel happy or feel fulfilled.* Again, that was just a pattern. Now I love doing one thing at a time and enjoying it fully. I limit myself to the amount of people I work with per day (I know my energetic limit). I also learned to say to my family, loved ones, and clients, "I'm too tired to do this now." This is a whole lot better than having to collapse and/or having to disconnect and end up hurting anyone.

When love sits on emotions it can very quickly be feeling good or bad. In a relationship, one might be expected to do certain things to show their love. But that's not what love is. It's not a feeling! I was surprised when the guides told me that. How can it not be a feeling? Don't we feel love? Just like an orgasm, love is a state of being, a frequency. It's not a feeling.

Love is a frequency that contains all!

Love vibration contains forgiveness, acceptance, and allowance of meeting ourselves through another. Love is also forgiveness, allowance, and acceptance of ourselves by ourselves. Self-love is most important. The wisdom we get along the way, or during the relationship, is the success of the relationship. It's not the outcome that matters as much as that we keep getting deeper and unraveling the layers of us by looking in the mirror our partners, family, and loved ones hold up for us. We need a way of looking within and seeing what triggers us and why, how to overcome it, and how to increase our frequency.

Intimacy is the vessel of connection; it's the language of love. It starts with listening, choosing, staying true to what we desire, and being creative. In touching one another, we exchange or transfer energies. Many times, it's energies that are not verbalized. Intimacy is not only sexual, and it's not only between partners. It's between two human beings.

If we look at intimacy as a discharge (orgasm only), we do not get the knowledge (the information transfer).

Contraction is the shadow side of love—allowing only a little bit in. When we play roles for each other, we're disconnected from true love. It causes us to miss the true giving and receiving.

Love is and has creation in it. A soul's center contains only itself—the full connection to itself. Happiness and joy are the stories of love in the light. That is why it's important for us to be happy, to follow our joy. This is when we get creative and fulfilled.

THE PRACTICE

TOOLS FOR LOVE:

1. Look deeper into your partner's eyes and see what's going on. Is he or she open to listening? You can also do this with your children.

2. Do you allow yourself to grow or do you contract yourself from a place of: *There is no (or not enough) money, time, or possibilities?* How do you live? Do you dare? Do you touch or come closer to what you want or desire? Do you grow from a spiritual perspective?

We're not here to accumulate material things. We're here to allow the energy of our journey to unfold. The journey is about more light, growth, and connection!

3. Sing to yourself. Connect to your joy daily. Joyfulness and happiness birth creativity and abundance. There is no reason to work long hours, it makes us lose our center. We need to touch and listen to create and grow spiritually.

4. Lastly, just as important—make a personal declaration about what it is you want or desire in the next step in your life, or even for the day about to start. It doesn't need to be the same every day. Put your hand on your heart so your attention or energy creation comes from there (not from your head), listen in, and come from a new place each day. *Today my heart will smile, dance, or get excited to_____.* Do you feel expanded when you think of doing that? Do you connect to the excitement within?

As you get into the habit of checking in, you could do it for every aspect of your life. Stay creative and centered, love and accept yourself unconditionally and all else will fall into place.

Sharon Joseph has professionally coached people in their personal growth for close to 20 years. She is a channeler, healer, bestselling author, medium, animal communicator, DNA architect, and a clairvoyant.

Sharon is a mirror for others to explore and embrace who they are, supporting them as they step into the fullness of their being. Using her astute medical intuition (x-ray vision), she can interpret the language of the body when it comes to ailments and or energetic blocks. She gives down-to-earth tools on how to release these blocks, and uses her fast and powerful healing ability to assist in healing. She also uses her clairvoyance, energy interpretation, and her gift as a medium to help one upgrade their awareness and life. Sharon helps people uncover and focus on what they can accomplish in any area of life, including personal growth, health, love, relationships, success and career.

Sharon achieved a bachelor's degree in computer science with a minor in business as well as a Ph.D. in Metaphysical Science. She is an ordained minister. As a citizen of the world, Sharon respects all paths to the One. Her passions include animals, laughing, dancing, travel, meditation, and connecting with like-minded people.

She is currently guiding people to release their old stories on all levels and step into their joy. She does it through one-on-one sessions, classes (online and in person), and she also conducts retreats around the world.

Connect with Sharon:

Website: www.sharonjosef.com

Email: sharonjosef8@gmail.com

Facebook: https://www.facebook.com/SharonNitka/

Instagram: https://www.instagram.com/sharonjo/

Twitter: https://twitter.com/sharonJ84151501

LinkedIn: https://www.linkedin.com/in/sharon-josef-04896a7a/

"We come into this life experience knowing our worth and loving ourselves, but then our environment (parents, teachers, friends) teaches us conditional love."

~ Sharon Josef, Ph.D

CHAPTER 13

YOU'RE MAGNETIC
USE REIKI POWER TO ATTRACT THE LOVE YOU NEED

Dr. Makeba Morgan Hill, Reiki Queen

MY STORY

I married my ex-husband for all the wrong reasons. We were not in love.

What happened? How did I end up here? Is this what the rest of my life is supposed to feel like? I'm just in my 40s! How is it that I'm married, yet still feel so lonely? Am I supposed to just live like my love life doesn't matter?

If any of these thoughts resonate with you, this chapter is dedicated to you. For anyone who has ever felt alone, especially while in a romantic relationship, I'm sorry. I know how you feel. Don't settle. You deserve to be loved. You are magnetic and the practice of Reiki energy healing can help raise your vibration, so you can start attracting more of what you need.

LET'S GET MARRIED!

I wanted my child to grow up in a two-parent home because I didn't. My parents separated when I was 11, and I took it hard. I didn't understand why they weren't together and why, all of a sudden, I had a broken home. I blamed my father and judged my mother. I vowed that would never happen to me.

At 28 years old, my college sweetheart and I broke up. He was the love of my life at the time. After having a few failed short-term relationships after the breakup, I didn't have the words to describe the panic I felt.

I'll never find love again. I'll never have kids. I'm destined to have a failed marriage like "everyone" else in my family. I'm not good enough, smart enough, pretty enough.

It was the ultimate negative self-talk. I was so focused on my grim future and perceived inadequacies, that I was barely present during my late twenties. I was totally in my head and felt lost.

Around that time, I met Tim at a birthday barbecue for a guy I was casually dating. He said, "Hey, dance with me." I said, "No. I'm here with the birthday boy. That might be a little awkward," and laughed as I smiled coyly. He was cute, so we talked, laughed, danced a little, exchanged numbers, and started dating, eventually.

It was a rocky relationship from the start. I didn't love myself when we met. My confidence was low, and I was looking for a relationship to make me whole. I didn't know where I stood with him. We never formally declared we were a couple. A year and a half later, after several breakups and makeups, I discovered I was pregnant.

My father urged me to "do the right thing," while my mother reiterated her mantra over and over again, "You know you don't need a man, right?" It didn't matter that my ex-husband never told me he loved me during our courtship or that we had a shaky dating relationship. I married him anyway. At the time, I didn't think I could do better. I married a man who would never truly, fully love me. I did this because he asked, and I wanted to "do the right thing" for my daughter.

He proposed when Meredith was a couple of weeks old. I planned the wedding hastily because I didn't want him to change his mind. We got married seven months later, and I quickly realized I had made a bad decision. I thought things would be different once we were married. I thought he'd declare his love for me. I thought we'd be a good team. I thought we'd spend time together. I thought my needs would be fulfilled. I thought I'd adjust or that he'd change, but he didn't change, and neither did I. I remember him shouting, "Why did you marry me anyway?" And I recalled thinking: *I have no earthly idea.*

Fast-forward 14 years—my daughter and I had a conversation that went something like this:

"Mom," she said, "I don't feel like Daddy loves me. He doesn't see me or hear me. He doesn't pay me any attention. He always seems so annoyed with me."

Disgusted, I could relate and said, "Really? That's how I feel. You shouldn't feel like that, though. He's your father. He loves you." I married him, so she could have a relationship with him and it backfired. I felt so stupid.

That's when I realized the issue was deeper than my romantic relationship with my husband. He didn't know how to love us because he didn't truly love himself. And I stayed for my daughter because I didn't want to be a failure. *I chose this life, so I should just stick with it.*

By then, I had grown a callus around my heart. It was numb.

I'm a Cancer. We're lovers. Hell, I'm a lover of love. I'm a love bug, a cuddle muffin, all the things, and here I am in this space. My life just feels so. . . loveless.

My back ached in the heart space because of the loneliness. I felt helpless. As an empath, it felt odd not to feel anything for my husband. The anxiety I felt over the years crept back up. I was not getting the love I needed.

WAKE-UP CALL!

We made it to my daughter's high school graduation. She was heading to college. *What will I do now? She gave me purpose. She was my joy—my company keeper.* My internal light felt dim and desperate. I tried yoga, meditation, isolation, associations—anything to stay busy and protect myself from the lack of love at home. I was doing all right, I thought.

One day an old friend called. He was in town and wanted to meet to talk. He said, "Keeb, it's been a long time! How've you been?" I said, "I'm living."

We had a history. He knew me well a long time ago. My lack of enthusiasm was palpable. He looked deeply into my eyes, searching my soul. He tilted his head and said, "What's that mean?"

We walked and talked. We laughed and cried. We were both going through similar things at home. He reached for my hand. The sudden surge of energy I felt when our hands touched sent what felt like a jolt of lightning through my body. I was nervous. I thought I might be having a heart attack, literally. My breathing was sporadic. I felt lightheaded. The dead battery in my chest was suddenly recharged. I remembered what it felt like to feel again.

When I encountered my friend that warm summer day and he touched my hand, my heart chakra opened. That moment ignited my healing journey. Neither of us knew that at the time, but it was truly a blessing. That was Reiki.

That was the beginning of my personal enlightenment and return to self-love. At that moment, things changed for me. I began to write again. I began to listen to music and see in color again. I saw beauty in the mirror. I was more attuned to the energy in others. I realized how sensitive I was to negativity and how bruised I was by it. I searched for ways to nurture my energy and made a decision to put myself first. I was wide open.

I began to attract so much positivity. I was a catalyst for change in my own life and good things began to flow toward me. I'm sharing this story so that you, too, may move further along on your path to enlightenment using Reiki as a self-healing tool.

THE PRACTICE

YOU ARE MAGNETIC

The Law of Attraction states that positive or negative thoughts bring positive or negative experiences into a person's life.

Have you ever thought something like, *oh, it would suck if it rained today,* and, inevitably, it rained? Or you thought, *I feel so fat,* and you proceeded to sabotage your weight loss plan with pizza and a pint of ice cream?

This type of negative thought creates negative outcomes. Think positive. Change the narrative. What would happen if you thought, *The weather will be just what we need today,* or *I'm beautiful just the way I am?*

The first step in reclaiming love in your life is to change thoughts and practices that lead to negative outcomes. We tend to dwell on the negative when things don't go our way. A paradigm shift is in order to realize our full magnetic potential.

Reiki energy healing helps to focus the mind on the light inside of us, which makes it a lot more difficult to focus on and dwell on negativity. This helps to raise our magnetism for attracting the good stuff.

WHAT IS REIKI?

According to the dictionary, "Reiki is a healing technique based on the principle that the therapist can channel energy into the patient using touch, to activate the natural healing processes of the patient's body and restore physical and emotional well-being."

We are energetic beings. All humans can move and transfer energy within, around, and amongst ourselves. The practice of moving the universal life energy, i.e., Reiki, in a person's body doesn't require special training. We all have the power to be a vessel of energy.

Reiki is an amazing tool used to move the universal life force within one's body. It helps with chakra alignment so people and animals can do the work to continue their own healing. Training and attunement allow us to be stronger, more directed, and more knowledgeable about the practice. Therefore, training or working with a trained practitioner is highly recommended.

HOW CAN REIKI HELP?

As a Reiki practitioner, I can sense when chakras are out of sorts. With the power in my hands, I can unstick stagnant energy. I'm told that during a session, my clients feel heat, tingling, and/or a sense of calm. Some cry to release pain or uncertainty. Some cry joyful tears because they understand why they were feeling the way they were feeling. They leave my table with recommendations and a way forward.

Many Reiki practitioners, including myself, call upon God, the Universe, spirits, and/or ancestors to guide our hands as we practice this work. It's serious business! During my practice, I call directly on God to help me assess and guide my clients. He is always eager to help. He wants to connect more with his people. My practice allows deep connections with

God, the inner soul, and the spirit realm. These connections are a constant reminder that we are not alone, even when we think we are. *We are not alone.*

REIKI FOR LOVE

When I became a Reiki practitioner, a whole new world opened up to me. I began practicing self-healing at least once a day and could immediately feel changes in my body. Self-healing connects you with the "self." When I hover my hands over my body, I say: *Hello, Self. I love you and God loves you, too, and there's nothing you can do about it.* I'm immediately calmer, my intuition heightens, I can manage my sensitivity, and I can be present for others. Practicing self-healing facilitates self-love. Self-love ignites our light and makes us a beacon.

Reiki with others connects you at the "spirit" level. An early example for me was after scanning my daughter's body and consulting with God and the spirits; I was able to open and align her throat, heart, and sacral chakras. She was having trouble in college and during our session, I was able to get clarity on her future career. We learned what school she should attend. I was able to share insights about her soulmates and other spiritual connections. We cried together so deeply during that session. Our spirits were united and our love for each other amplified!

Since then, I have done the same for many people. I give people practical exercises to maintain alignment and facilitate their healing. You can do it, too. Reiki is an effective means of gaining alignment spiritually, emotionally, and physically, and since love is the universal antidote, that is my focus.

LET'S RAISE YOUR VIBRATION!

Do you ever feel lost or alone? Do you ever feel that you're not worthy of being loved? Do you ever feel the people around you who are supposed to love you are just not cutting the mustard? Do you worry so much about the future and finding love that it cripples you sometimes? Have you gotten so used to not feeling that you think it's normal? You need love. We all need love. We need love in the same way that we need food and water. Don't deny yourself.

Below are a few exercises you can do to help raise your vibration, so you can attract the love you need in your life.

Ask yourself the following questions. Be honest. How do you feel about your answers? Are there obvious areas that need improvement? Do something about it. Find it within yourself to love yourself and others.

Sacral Chakra Assessment – What's Your Pleasure?

1. Am I satisfied with my love life?
2. When was the last time I was truly happy?
3. Is my career truly my passion?
4. Am I doing things that bring me joy in love and in life?
5. How am I expressing my creativity in my daily life?

Heart Chakra Assessment – Who Do You Love?

1. Do I deserve to be loved? What kind of conditions, if any, do I put on myself or others to receive love?
2. Is there something I need to forgive myself for that is preventing me from loving myself fully?
3. Is there something I need to forgive someone else for that has made it difficult for me to give or receive love?
4. What makes my heart sing? Search your soul.

Crown Chakra Assessment – How Connected Are You?

1. What does peace look and feel like for you?
2. How often do you take time to just be quiet? Be still? Reflect? Relax?
3. What activities or practices do you or can you employ to feel more connected to a higher power, to yourself, and to others?

Mirror Work

Incorporate positive self-talk, tapping, and basic Reiki hand movements into your daily routine. This is best done first thing in the morning, preferably as you're preparing for the day.

1. Stand in front of your mirror.
2. Look deeply into your eyes.
3. Look at your face, then return your gaze to your eyes.
4. Say, "Good morning, Beautiful. Today is your day. You are special. You are loved. You are blessed."

5. Take both of your hands and hover them over the top of your head.

6. Tap your head lightly three times.

7. Breathe.

8. Move your hands down to the front of your face. Your palms should be facing you; fingertips should be hovering in front of your third eye, i.e., the center of your forehead and your palms should be toward your chin.

9. Tap your forehead with your fingertips three times.

10. Breathe.

11. Place your hands over your heart with your right hand close to your body and the left hand over the right.

12. Lightly tap your right fingertips on your chest for three sets of three.

13. Breathe deeply between sets.

14. Ask God for love, guidance, support, forgiveness, and fun in your day. Amen.

Meditation

Prayer and meditation offer an opportunity to reset, refocus, and seek guidance from a higher power. I suggest making time twice a day, every day to do this, even if it is only for five or ten minutes. You can do it before you get out of bed in the morning and right after you go to sleep. Please see my six-minute guided meditation with Reiki energy healing. Breathe with me https://youtu.be/csPO-9-BakM.

Next Steps

These self-healing activities are a start. There are many other ways that you can get your energy moving to attract the love you need. This is what I want you to do right now.

- Remove toxicity from your life. This includes activities and people!

- Pay more attention to your thought patterns. Negative thoughts breed negative outcomes. Try positive affirmations.

- Don't settle. Know you deserve love. Know you are not made to be without happiness. Know your search for love and satisfaction starts within you.

- Accept the fact that you deserve to be loved in a way that feeds your soul.
- Ask God to show you the light within you.

You can't heal if you pretend that you're not hurt. Do the work to heal yourself, so your light can shine. When your light shines, light, love, happiness, joy, and bliss ultimately find their way to you. You're magnetic!

Dr. Makeba Morgan Hill, affectionately known as Dr. Makeba, the Doctor of Love, wears many hats, as do many women. She is a writer, a Reiki master, a yogi in the making, a health care executive, an entrepreneur, a friend, a mother, a teacher, an extreme cat lover, a believer that children are our future, and a child of God.

Dr. Makeba owns Dr. Makeba & Friends Healing Hands, which is a holistic wellness center based in Atlanta, Georgia, that specializes in modalities to facilitate balance in the body, mind, and soul for humans and their pets. Using the power of love and light generated through her Reiki energy work and her spiritual connections, she helps souls experience much-needed breakthroughs in all aspects of their lives.

As an empath who cares deeply for others, Dr. Makeba has been drawn to non-profit caring and learning industries throughout her career, where she has most often served in strategic planning or executive leadership roles. She earned a bachelor's in Healthcare Management from Florida A&M University, a Master of Health Services Administration degree from George Washington University, and a doctorate in higher education at the University of Georgia.

A believer in continuing education, she is a Reiki Master with certifications in Usui, Karuna Ki, Kundalini, Gold, and Divine Fire methods. She's currently a student of Radiance Sutras School of Meditation to become a certified meditation instructor, and she is also working on becoming a certified sex and intimacy coach. In addition, Dr. Makeba founded and runs Havenly Hills Cat House, a volunteer organization dedicated to the care and keeping of community cats entrusted to her neighbor in Atlanta.

Dr. Makeba is doing her part to bring love and light back to the world. Love is the secret sauce.

Connect with Dr. Makeba:

Website: https://drmakeba4love.com/

LinkedIn: https://www.linkedin.com/in/dr-makeba-morgan-hill-7598394/

Facebook: https://www.Facebook.com/DrMakeba4Love

Linktree: https://www.linktr.ee/drmakeba4love/

Twitter: https://www.Twitter.com/drmakeba4love

YouTube: DrMakeba4Love

"Love is the universal antidote. If you seek love within first, you will never be without."

~ Dr. Makeba Morgan Hill

CHAPTER 14

A JOURNEY THROUGH CO-DEPENDENCE
HEALING WITH SELF-LOVE AND RESPECT

Rosalind Beresford

I've always hated the term co-dependent. *What is it about me that contributes to another person's addiction? How is my life dependent on that person's addiction?* It took years of therapy, coaching, and self-development practices to learn the truth about my co-dependence.

MY STORY

It was 1972. I was ten years old and the terror I thought we left behind was raging through my body. I was called out of class to the principal's office. My stomach knotted. I couldn't believe my eyes. The man waiting for me in the office looked even more terrifying than I remembered. His face was mottled with cuts and bruises. I feared this man. I knew he was capable of violence.

The principal said, "Your dad needs to talk to you."

"I was in a little helicopter accident," he said when we were alone. I gulped but didn't say a word. "I want to know where you live. I want to visit with you and your siblings."

He showed up at our apartment later that evening. We were all called to the living room.

Mom said, "Your father wants to know if you want him to be part of our lives."

The seven of us were lined up from oldest, at 15 years, to youngest, not even five yet. Each of us answered, some defiantly, some fearfully. When it was my turn, I echoed my older siblings with a quaver in my voice. "No."

When it was the youngest's turn, tearfully he reached for a hug from my father. His gesture was rebuffed by my father: "You might as well stop loving me, too."

My heart shattered for my little brother. He still loved his father and was too young to fully grasp what was happening.

I don't know for certain if that was when my co-dependent thinking began, but I do know that childhood trauma and living with an alcoholic parent can trigger co-dependent thinking.

My childhood consisted of the before times when we lived with my abusive, raging alcoholic father, my early teen years as caretaker of my younger siblings, and my teen years as the peacekeeper, who made sure the house was in order so that when mom got home from work, there wouldn't be any reason for her to lose her temper. Fast forward to my married life and the pattern continued.

When my son was four, I discovered something I didn't want to accept about my husband. He had another identity, created so he could seek sexual encounters with other women. My caretaker brain kicked in. *I need to help him. He has lost his way and we need to find a path to repair our broken marriage.*

We began weekly sessions with a marriage counselor. During therapy, we explored our different sex and intimacy styles. What I took away from this therapy was that my more conservative approach to sex was the problem. I opened my mind to explore my own sexuality. I made changes. Don't get me wrong—I was happy to discover this side of me. Ultimately though, I was doing this to please him.

These changes allowed me to maintain my role as a caretaker. This thinking also allowed me to wear blinders.

Four years later, we moved to another new country. The kids were with their grandparents. My husband and I celebrated the new home purchase and the move. The celebration was amazing. I was smiling, content, and excited. Our marriage was stronger than ever.

Later that night, I was flipping through the photos of our new home on his camera. My heart stopped and then began beating faster and faster. I had trouble breathing. There was a picture of another woman.

On some level, I knew this was not my problem. This was his problem.

I confronted him. "You need to fix this. You need to find a therapist to figure out why I'm not enough for you." I got on a plane and flew to Canada to be with our kids for the summer. I didn't have a clue about what I was going to do. I just knew I couldn't take it anymore.

He began to see a therapist by himself. Four weeks later he convinced me to join him and bring the kids for a visit. His hands were shaking as we explored the city with the kids. He looked so defeated. For some reason, I still loved this man, and I knew we could make this work. I could make this work.

Five years later, we were in yet another new country. I can't remember what made me suspicious, but I began figuring out ways to monitor his computer use. I discovered that not only was he carrying on with his sexual explorations, but he never really stopped. Somehow, I adopted another co-dependent personality trait—I ignored signs. I made excuses for all the behaviors I now recognized as him covering his tracks.

I kicked into caretaker mode. There was some media coverage of famous people with sex addictions. *Was this his problem? Did he have a sex addiction?*

I took control again. I started researching the topic and concluded that I was dealing with an addict. I found a therapist who specializes in treating sex addicts. My stomach was in knots, but I somehow found the courage to talk to him about it.

"I love you, but I can't go on like this. Your behavior is out of control. It is ruining us. I think you may have a problem we can't solve on our own. No matter what we've tried in the past you can't seem to stop. It's like an addiction. You need to get help."

He was contrite. "I love you too. I swear I want to save the marriage." He told me exactly what a co-dependent needs to hear. "I will get help. I don't want to lose what we have."

He agreed to see the therapist. He even went to a few sex addicts' anonymous meetings. After about six weeks he announced, "I'm not like those other people in the meetings. I have learned how to control myself. I don't need help anymore."

I panicked. I didn't believe him. Once again, I jumped into caretaker mode.

"I get it that this is not easy. I need to know that you want to change. I'm broken. My trust is broken. I need to know that you are willing to do the work to repair us."

He agreed to see the therapist as a couple. It was hard work. There were lots of tears. His discomfort with the therapy was palpable. Nothing was resolved because he eventually refused to continue. I was in a downward spiral of despair.

How could he not see my pain? How could he not be willing to do the work to make us better? Why can't he see how important this is to me? He obviously doesn't care enough about me. He doesn't respect my needs. I can't go on like this. I need help. I am dying inside.

A month later, I began seeing the therapist solo. He was okay with that. I'm not sure what he thought it would accomplish. I didn't know what it would accomplish. I just knew I needed help.

The therapist was amazing, but when she started broaching the topic of my upbringing, my response went something like this:

"Yeah, I had a lousy childhood, but I'm a fully functioning, grown adult now. I don't want to delve into it. It's in the past and has no bearing on this." I was in denial.

Eventually, we did some inner child work. I learned to experience the feelings of my inner child and to provide comfort to her. I was able to talk to my father (who died in 1986), as my younger self, to tell him about my hurt and how frightened I was of him.

After a year of therapy, I finally felt confident enough to re-establish my own identity as a strong, independent woman. I upgraded my educational credentials and went back to work outside the home for the first time in 15 years.

My confidence grew. My ability to calm my inner fears grew. My identity as a person beyond the wife of a sex addict grew. I wasn't 100% healed, but I was well enough that I could finally break away from my marriage of 30-plus years to start over. I was still a mess in many ways.

I was very much still in denial that I had a co-dependent personality. I could not see how I had contributed to his addiction. *I didn't tell my spouse to go out and have sex with strangers. I wasn't dependent on his sexual exploits.*

If the light side of being co-dependent is that it fulfills my need to be a nurturer, then how can being a co-dependent person be such a bad thing? I can see that it's a bad thing for the addict because it allows him or her to continue the addictive behavior. But why is it a bad thing to be a nurturer?

About a year after I left him to start over in my home country, I attended a women's retreat. That retreat opened my eyes to my co-dependent behaviors. The coach facilitating the retreat helped me see that my co-dependency was manifesting itself in my need to nurture other people—including my ex-husband. It controlled so many of my decisions over the years. Ironically, I needed to learn to nurture myself to break the cycle of co-dependency.

I began more intensive journaling, meditating, using affirmations, and focusing on the many things in my life for which I was grateful. With all these practices I learned to nurture and love myself. This doesn't exclude my natural nurturer tendencies toward other people. It just places my need for self-love in line with my need to nurture those around me. I learned that loving someone doesn't mean that I must be swallowed whole by their problems. You can learn this, too.

THE PRACTICE

Now when I work with clients who exhibit co-dependent behaviors, I confidently use all the tools that repaired my co-dependent thinking. I guide clients to use journaling, affirmations, and meditations.

1. Connect with your core values. Do what is meaningful to you. Stop deriving your self-worth through other people.

This can be done with the help of journaling. Write down what you believe is important to you. What makes you do what you do? Why is it important to you? Find opportunities to live by those values through volunteering, at home with your family, and if you're lucky, in the work you do.

Affirmation:

It is healthy to have my own ideas, feelings, interests, goals, and values.

2. Set boundaries. Get clear on what your needs are. If you said yes to something, and then later felt resentful about it, that's a sign that you have violated your own boundaries. Practice smart selfishness. Honor your needs, wants, and feelings. Communicate your needs, wants, and boundaries.

Go back to those journal entries you made about your core values. Use these as a guide to set boundaries in your life. Record some of your boundaries in your journal as you discover them. Getting them out of your head and physically writing them down makes them feel more real.

Affirmation:

Saying no does not make me a bad person.

3. Release outcomes. Learn to tolerate the possibility of disappointing people. You can't fix everybody. Stop trying.

Journal about times you tried to fix someone else's problem. How did that turn out? What could you have done differently that honored yourself and your love for the other person?

Affirmations:

I can't control other people. I can only control my reaction to them.

I can only manage my own life. It's not my job to fix other people.

4. Cultivate independence and confidence. Allow yourself to see more than just the pleasing, peacekeeping, and diplomatic you. Sign up to receive my free "8 Steps to Grow your Self Confidence" https://www.triskeliontransitions.com/

Affirmations:

Taking care of others shouldn't come at my own expense.

I am powerful, and I love it.

I know that I count, and I act as if I do.

My self-worth does not depend on other people

It is okay to prioritize my own well-being.

5.   Connect with your inner child and help them heal.

In your journal, write letters to the people who harmed your inner child. Tell them about the hurt and how it has manifested itself throughout your life. Have a conversation with your inner child to tell them you will take care of them. Remind them that they are safe and protected. This might best be done with the guidance of a therapist or coach who specializes in dealing with childhood trauma.

Practice self-soothing techniques, such as this self-kindness meditation:

Get comfortable. Don't close your eyes but do soften your gaze. It might help if you can look out a window or light a candle to draw your focus. Find something physical you can hold that comforts you, such as a warm blanket or a beloved pet. Take several deep cleansing breaths and repeat the following phrases.

Your feelings are valid. They make you human.

You are strong, and you can move through this pain.

You are safe, and you are loved.

You are safe, and I love you.

6.   The final tool I'm going to share with you is the loving-kindness mediation. This is the tool that I found the most powerful and the most healing. It helped me develop a strong sense of self-worth and allowed me to forgive the people in my life who took advantage of my co-dependent behaviors.

This style of meditation requires nothing special and has no time requirements. However, consider where you'd like to practice it. Continuing with the idea of building confidence starting from the outside, choose a supportive chair or lie down on the floor to give you a physical representation of confidence. It might help to cover yourself with a weighted or warm blanket to help you feel as if you're being hugged.

Next, begin with deep belly breaths to help you relieve tension in your body and help you sink more into the support around you.

Then repeat each of the following sentences—saying them out loud is helpful, but if that feels awkward, unnatural, or scary to you, say them silently. You can write them down when you first begin. I did.

- *May I be free from inner and outer harm.*
- *May I be happy.*
- *May I be healthy.*
- *May I live with ease.*
- *May I experience love and joy.*
- *May I be free from pain and suffering.*

At first, I couldn't complete even the first two thoughts without crying, and I would become flooded with emotion and unable to continue.

Whatever emotions you experience, know they're okay.

What moves me with the loving-kindness meditation is that it can be expanded to include others. You can also use this meditation to help you practice loving kindness toward those who have harmed you. It's a very loving meditation, as the name suggests.

For example, you might say this:

- *May (insert name of spouse, mother, neighbor, friend, etc.) be free from inner and outer harm.*
- *May _____ be happy.*
- *May _____ be healthy.*
- *May _____ live with ease.*
- *May _____ experience love and joy.*
- *May _____ be free from pain and suffering.*

With continued practice, I could expand the meditation and believe I deserved everything it said. I could even include my ex-husband in the meditation. This was incredibly difficult at first; emotions flooded me and there were many tears. But it got easier as time went on and I began to see my ex-husband, my father, and my mother as merely human, not purposefully hurtful to me.

I encourage you to try out some of the mediations and affirmations with the help of my YouTube Channel: https://bit.ly/3BKpMA4

Remember, your journey through co-dependency leads to self-love and respect. Namaste.

Rosalind is a life coach, co-host of the Relentless Transitions Podcast, and the Founder of Triskelion Transitions. She helps clients transform that scared little voice in their heads into a chorus of self-empowerment.

By the time she was 17 years old, she had moved towns and neighborhoods ten times. As a wife and mother, she moved nine times—seven of those moves were international. In her early 50s she started over as a divorcee. She learned from a young age how to transition to a new life and knows how to start over and reinvent herself.

Her ideal clients are women in transition who have reached a point in life where they ask themselves, "What's next?"; "How do I start over?"

She is an accredited professional Integral Coach™ and is certified to administer the EQi-2.0 and EQ360 assessments. She is a member of the International Coaching® Federation.

Fun fact: As a child she always wanted to learn to dance but didn't have the money to pay for lessons. As an adult, she has taken ballet, belly dancing, and ballroom dancing lessons. She still can't dance, but she has fun trying.

Connect with Rosalind:

For more information, go to https://linktr.ee/TriskelionTransitions

Website: info@triskeliontransitions.com

"As a co-dependent it feels redeemable to pick up the pieces to guide the addict towards healing solutions, but in doing so, you lose sight of who you are. You need to learn to love yourself as much as you love the addict."

~ Rosalind Beresford

CHAPTER 15

SOUL GUIDANCE
LEARNING TO LISTEN, TRUST, AND ACT ON YOUR INNER WISDOM

Kye Sun Rose

MY STORY

"Kye, if you're driving, pull over; Alan died last night. He went peacefully in his sleep."

I just returned from vacation down south. It was Easter Sunday, and as I finished visiting my horse and left the barn, my spiritual teacher and dear friend Alan called in. Of course, I picked up the call, but it was his husband, Jim.

I was shocked, devastated, and in complete disbelief over the news of his unexpected death. I would never have imagined his passing would lead me to my best life.

I had 37 patients scheduled the following day. I couldn't cancel. Thank God for the Covid protocol requiring me to wear a mask, as it hid the pain and disbelief on my face. Later as I drove home, I was in a daze. I saw myself slowly veer out of my lane, and suddenly this scratchy, banging noise came through the radio.

What the hell is that God-awful noise? This car is brand new. Is that you, Alan?

I quickly re-entered my body and somehow avoided side-swiping the car next to me, and even had time to get safely to my exit. At that moment, I sensed Alan sitting in the passenger seat, giving me that smirk you only get from your teacher. From that moment on, I accepted his death a little more, knowing he was close and would be there if I needed him.

Honestly, I was miserable. I desperately wanted to start my energy healing and coaching practice for years. I cut back to a three-day workweek seeing patients and opened a healing center in the in-law space in my house. I was too comfortable. I loved the free time. I was financially abundant and enjoyed spending time at the barn riding my horse. Yet, inside I was distraught. I was stuck, frozen with fear of building a practice independently.

I felt like a failure for not building the business so I could eventually leave the dermatology practice. But with Alan's death, something awoke inside of me. I heard the words of Wayne Dyer.

Don't die with your music inside you.

By the end of that week, I decided to leave the practice where I had spent the last 26 years.

Trust. All will be okay. Trust. All will be okay.

I kept hearing this over and over. I knew I had to leave the safety of my job, but I had no clients.

How would I make ends meet?

Trust. All will be okay.

It took six months to leave, but I did it. When fear reared its ugly head, I instantly heard:

Trust. All will be okay.

Alan's dying helped me do something I may never have done alone. How did I have the courage to make this leap? I trusted that voice with every ounce of my being because of my time on the Red Road.

It all started when I was 37 years old. I was becoming increasingly depressed. I thought I had it all. I was in a five-year relationship with a woman and was planning to have a child. Yet, I could not truly commit to any of it. I felt incapable of fully opening my heart. I struggled with feeling loved and worthy of the dream of creating a family. Finally, I left the relationship and decided to see a therapist. I drove by this building every day on my way to work. I watched the shop open for business. The sign that went up read, "Heaven to Earth." A soft, wispy voice inside often said, *someday I'm going to go in there.*

I did go in. The therapist just lost her Native American teacher in Texas, moved back to Massachusetts, and opened her practice. She was different than other therapists I knew. She ran a weekly prayer group, and I joined. I loved praying out loud from my heart. It felt right. She also led a sweat lodge a few hours away, and I felt pulled to go. My spiritual life came alive in that shop.

It was winter. For my first lodge, it was cold and icy. We spent most of the day gathering rocks, covering the lodge, building a fire, and getting stuck in the deep mud melting around the blazing fire that seemed alive. Yet, being outside in nature was exhilarating.

When it was time to enter the sweat lodge, crawling upon the frozen ground, I felt at home. The sweat lodge is a purification ceremony. The lodge represents the womb of Mother Earth. Respectfully, you crawl in on your hands and knees, and when you leave, you do the same, but you emerge reborn.

It was cold, but I warmed up as the fireman gingerly placed the hot rocks in the center of the lodge called the altar. The door flap was closed, and it was pitch black. The stones glowed red, sizzled, and sang their tunes.

Some people get anxious in the darkness of the lodge, leave, and never return. The lodge is a place to heal and be with yourself and your Creator. This dark, sweaty, hot place was strange yet very comforting. The water pourer, her husband, sat at the door and ran the ceremony. He made the prayers and poured water on the rocks to create the steam that purifies the body and the spirit. His prayers held a truth I faintly already knew. As she sang the ceremonial songs, they filled me with a sense of home. So many people come and feel like they have lived this life before as part of the land's original peoples. I felt this as well.

I heard a voice say; she *is to be your teacher.*

What does that mean?

I had no idea, but I knew I would buy a nice blanket and a small package of tobacco, pray into it, and present it to her. I was uncertain how she'd respond. But I knew I was here to heal my core issues, feel love in my heart, and feel worthy of love. Finally, she and her husband said yes and took on four students.

The hard work began. As students, we played out our patterns and emotional issues with each other stemming from our family of origin. We spent hours unraveling root issues, learning to listen, speak to each other, and resolve conflict. Yet, thanks to our teachers, we always left feeling loved and acknowledged.

As a student, I was to learn and sing the Lakota songs in the lodge. One day in the darkness of the lodge, I was so scared, yet I sang the song as expected. It felt good to open my throat chakra, and I felt more confident. During the silence, I saw myself as a little infant suddenly waking up from the dead. First, the baby was flaccid, and then she came alive. It was exhilarating. I knew to hold her and love her. It was the first step in being able to love and feel loved.

I loved the Vision Quest ceremony. It's a four-year commitment. I first supported and then quested for many years. You go out in nature, sit on a blanket and fast from food and water for up to four days. Then, you pray for a vision for your life. The energy is more intense in high ceremonies; miracles happen even if one supports the ceremony.

As students, our core issues arose and played out amongst each other. I had yet to learn ceremony was gentler if I listened to that voice in my head saying:

I am so pissed off right now; I need help.

But, of course, I repeatedly ignored that guidance from deep within and waited until the proverbial two-by-four hit me over the head.

One day at Vision Quest, the energy of the ceremony was high, and a bunch of new people showed up. Unfortunately, I felt my emotions getting out of control as hunger and fatigue set in and chaos arose, usually around the silliest things.

Geez, that is so stupid how she is cutting those carrots.

I was projecting my feelings onto my spiritual sister as she was my safest target. Unfortunately, this silliness led to hurt feelings for both of us while preparing the meal for the supporters.

Moments later, as I washed the dishes in the pristine stainless-steel commercial kitchen, a giant three-foot cooking utensil fell from above and bonked me on my head. My spiritual sister and I cracked up laughing. Moments before, she was the object of my very negative feelings.

After that instance, I learned to trust my inner guidance and address issues sooner with my teacher out of respect and love for my spiritual sister. The ceremony was far more enjoyable when I listened to that subtle inner voice and acted on its guidance.

I loved the Red Road. In Lakota, Great Spirit (The Creator) is Wakan Tanka, meaning sacred buffalo. To the Lakota, the buffalo were sacred, and they gave the people everything to survive and thrive. I loved the teachings. Everything in nature is wakan (wah-kahn), meaning sacred. The trees are wakan, and the stones are wakan. They offer themselves for our sweat lodge ceremony. The animals are wakan, the insects are wakan, the rain is wakan, and the thunder is wakan. The sun and the moon are wakan. I am wakan, and you are wakan. We are all connected, and we are all one, represented by "Mitakuye Oyasin" (all my relations).

Our spiritual family was a Sundance family. Our leader was now a Sundance Chief. In the summers, we traveled to Arizona and South Dakota to attend the Sundance ceremonies. I loved visiting both reservations to attend the most powerful Lakota ceremony. The dancers fast from water and food for four days. They begin the dance before dawn and continue until late in the hot summer days while praying to the sun, representing Great Spirit. They offer prayers for the Earth, their families, and their communities for the coming year.

At the Arizona Sundance in the four corners area, you could see for miles across the flat land with mesas in the background. It was Hopi land, and it felt like home. The colors were spectacular muted reds and oranges. The male dancers would cut down and carry the tree of life into the Mystery Circle, where the ceremony occurred. I cried happy tears each time the tree was re-erected, adorned with hundreds of bright-colored swatches of material hanging from the branches holding the prayers of the dancers. My heart was open, and feeling love for the land and the people and the promise of the miracles ahead.

I made great strides in feeling and receiving love from my spiritual family. However, one morning I was helping prepare breakfast but was struggling, feeling depressed and alone. I was snippy to others who were just trying to help prepare breakfast for the supporters.

I'm not any help here. This sucks. I need to go into my tent and figure this out.

I now listened and obeyed that voice.

It felt vital for me to connect to and feel loved by the Creator. I could feel love from my spiritual family and my pets but couldn't feel love from Great Spirit. I tried desperately and failed. It was getting warm in the tent, and the dancers were walking in to begin the dance. I came out of my tent and sat alone in a chair, observing the dancers from afar.

I prayed nonstop for the dancers. Then, I suddenly felt something move up my back and stand behind me. I knew it was Tatanka Holy Man. He lives deep in the Earth and long ago turned himself into a buffalo and sacrificed his powers to help the Lakota people survive. I felt him turn into a buffalo, and suddenly I was on his back. He placed a buffalo robe on my back. We rode across the flat land aside hundreds of buffalo brothers and sisters.

"You are my sister, and these tatanka are your family. We love you and are here for you any time you need us."

I felt so much love and connection to Great Spirit from that moment on. It was a moment I will cherish forever.

Five years into the path, I became a Sundancer. While inside the Mystery Circle, a branch from the Tree of Life came down and hit my head. I asked an elder what that meant.

She said, "The tree of life wants you to dance."

Oh no, no way. I am not ready for that!

I approached my Chief. "I think the tree wants me to dance. I am not ready for that. It's a huge commitment."

I knew it would not just be a four-year commitment for me. My Chief says Sundance is a way of life, and deep down, I knew that.

He replied, "Go to the tree and ask why you should be dancing." So, I immediately went to the tree and prayed.

You have more healing to do.

Ugg, how could I argue with that reply?

I have danced for the last 15 years at Rosebud Reservation with my Chief and Sundance family under Chief Leonard Crowdog. I feel blessed to have shared the ceremony with people of all colors from all around the world.

Chief Crowdog believes we are all part of the Rainbow tribe. We will thrive because we come together and pray as one.

There were so many moments of healing on this path. They are wakan. There were also many laughs and fun times. I can't imagine who and where I would be if I disregarded that soft, subtle voice. It led me from a place of emptiness and depression to love and connectedness. It led me to fully trust in that voice, the voice of my soul.

The relentless guidance from that subtle, soft voice within led me to know I am loved and taught me to love and accept those around me. As a result, I have dedicated my life to being the highest vibration of love possible every moment, knowing I get to do it better every day.

In 2016, I created the Love Warrior Project so I could guide others to trust and act on the wisdom of their inner voice. Love Warriors follow their heart and soul's guidance to live their best lives.

Do you hear that voice?

THE PRACTICE

Follow Your Soul to Joy and Healing.

The soul speaks to us in a soft, subtle voice. We also have a loud and constant chattering voice of the mind. They are very different. Your soul will always try to keep you moving in the direction that serves your highest purpose. However, you may not always know what that is. Some learn early on to take notice of this voice, and others struggle to hear its guidance.

It will speak in different ways if ignored. You may lose something significant in your life to guide you toward your purpose. The loss may be a job, your health, or a loved one. Noticing the voice early on can help your life flow more gently.

If you feel a desire to start hearing the voice, you must connect to your soul.

Intention to connect to the soul is your first step. Your soul aches for you to hear the truth it holds for you.

Trusting in the guidance is part of the journey. It can be easy or not. That is up to you.

Acting on the guidance from your soul is the final step. Your soul wants you to live your best life, a life of flow and ease, abundance and joy.

It all starts with a desire to tune into your soul.

1. Let your Soul know you want to connect. I found connecting into joy was essential. It's as simple as doing something fun for 15 minutes daily. You may have to reflect on your younger years to recall what brought you joy. Maybe it's singing or dancing or reading or drawing. Perhaps it's walking outdoors or meditating or yoga, but only if you feel joy in this activity, not because it's good for you or because it means you're spiritual. So many times, we mix this up. What is good for us or seems spiritual is not the same as pure joy! Commit to two weeks of 15 minutes per day of a joyful experience. Your soul will know you desire to hear its guidance because you committed to be in joy daily.

2. Now that your soul knows you are serious about connecting, notice when and where you hear that voice come alive. Lean into these times. Is it when you are silent or when you are outdoors walking? Is it when you are swimming or running? I hear the voice when I drive in silence, walk the dog, and pray. Take the time to do this activity. You have opened the door for your soul to speak. Lean in and give it your full attention.

3. Keep a record of what your soul says. Consider a journal. The information is gold. I remember all the critical messages from the voice because it always directed me back on track when I veered off my path. It always appeared at the most auspicious time. The challenge is following the voice and doing what it says. It helps if you write it down. It's harder to disregard something you see in writing. You can have a deep conversation asking, why should I do this? See what wisdom your soul wants to share when you give it

to pen and paper. Listening gets easier; acting on the voice is for those serious about life's journey and purpose. Acting on your soul's guidance is like working a muscle. See yourself following the advice and improving as time goes by.

As a spiritual coach and healer, **Kye** is passionate about sharing her gift of ceremony and Native American teachings to help transform and heal your life. She uses the power and connection of the Divine within you to facilitate healing, allowing faster, gentler, and profound transformation.

In 1998, Kye became a student of Native American ceremonies following the Lakota traditions. She is a Pipe carrier and Sundancer. Kye offers a weekly healing pipe ceremony to guide others in healing their life through prayer and sacred songs.

Kye uses a multidimensional approach to gently remove old emotions and awaken the Divine Self that resides within us to live a purposeful life.

She is the founder of The Love Warrior Project, birthing Love Warriors to fully embrace the power of love within and guide them to love what they do and do it with love.

Connect with Kye:

Email: lovewarriorproject@comcast.net

Website: https://www.lovewarriorproject.com

Facebook: https://www.facebook.com/kyesunrose

To take part in Kye's Pipe Ceremony, visit:

https://wwwlovewarriorproject.coachesconsole.com/spirit-horse-healing-pipe-ceremony.html

"Love Warriors follow their heart's and soul's guidance to live their best lives."

~ Kye Sun Rose

CHAPTER 16

HONOR YOUR BEING
A GUIDE TO SELF-LOVE

Milagros Ruíz Bello, Curandera, Musical Healer, Theta Healer®

In honor of my grandmothers:
Manuela Martínez de Arámbula and Rosa Bello

MY STORY

Persistent feelings of doubt started coming up. *I have no idea how to love myself!* I paused with my hands folded in front of me. *How in the world am I going to write a chapter on love?!*

It was a peaceful morning in Big Bear, California, on Labor Day weekend. As I sat at the kitchen table wearing a comfy orange robe with my laptop open, a cup of coffee to my right, and a beautiful forest view to my left beyond the sliding glass door, I thought to myself, *what the hell did I get myself into!?*

I already started writing my chapter, and now I feel like such a fool for taking on this project. I have less than 20 days to complete this! Plus, people will think I'm a druggie for using plant medicine during some of my ceremonies. Not everyone will understand. I sat there with my hand on my forehead, looking out the glass door, lost and thinking about backing out. *I was on my knees just last night, realizing that I still don't know how to truly love myself. Yet here I am, writing about loving the self?!* After a couple of minutes of fighting with myself, I turned my attention again to my laptop and took a deep breath.

Fuck it! Here goes nothing.

I sat in ceremony the night before, and strong feelings of being a failure came rushing back up again. I sat on the living room floor crying my eyes out. *OMG, this ceremony wasn't even supposed to be for me. What is going on here?!* The thoughts kept coming in disbelief. Then, I let myself go. I realized I still felt guilty about how I raised my boys. *I wasn't there enough.* I kept having to grab tissues to blow my nose. "I didn't spend enough time with them," I said as the tears rolled out and down my cheeks. It was as if my heart was being squeezed by my own two hands. *Here, did you feel that? And how about this?!* I imagined myself squeezing out continual feelings of unworthiness. It was like I hated myself.

Looking back at my life, I never really knew what love was, so I was always attracted to toxic people. I had several partners. I was looking for love in all the wrong places. I was trying to fill a void I wasn't aware existed. Work, kids, man—that seemed to be my life. And when I wasn't with a man, I spent time out on a field playing softball or on a stage singing— again, filling a void. Not realizing I needed to look within.

Being bold and true is not the easiest goal to achieve. I keep having to read back each paragraph I write. I want to be as authentic and raw as I can be, even if it makes you, the reader, cringe. "Hi, I'm a hot mess. I'm now going to bare my soul to you. Love me or hate me, and nope, I'm not Little Miss Perfect, but I'm trying my best."

We tend to hide all the ugliness. We attempt to hide our past mistakes from the world and anyone new that comes into our lives. But why do this when our truth follows us *everywhere* and *will* resurface in time? Maybe it's the shame behind our actions. Maybe it's the "what will they say?" as if anyone is, in fact, perfect.

My void started way before I was born, but I won't bore you with those details now.

Welcome to my life.

I was molested as a child, raped at 14, and completely lost because I had no positive male role model. My mother was very naïve when she had me, so that didn't help matters. My father decided he wasn't ready to be a dad, so he abandoned me before I was born; then, three years later, he came looking for me. I didn't know I was feeling empty as I reached my teenage years. I sought attention, and although I was shy to a degree, I eventually enjoyed being on a stage, in the spotlight.

The stage welcomed me. But so did men. Toxic men.

After having my firstborn child at 17, traveling with a musical group, I got lost in the life of a performer. My mom was a true blessing as she would care for my son while I was gone on the weekends. *This,* to me, was the beginning of my pattern of regret. I was on the road on and off for several months. I missed almost a year of my son's toddler life because I was so caught up in the music world. I wanted to make it big! But when that didn't work out, karaoke was the next best thing.

During the following years, I worked up to two jobs, and I figured since my son would be asleep when I got home from work, *I'll just stop in at the bar for one song,* which would turn into two or three. *Wait, just one more.* Then I'd end up staying until closing time. This, although it may not sound so bad, was the unhealthy pattern that kept sinking me down into a non-productive world full of many paths leading nowhere.

Eventually, I was asked to sing with a top 40 band. This was yet another distraction. Another form of sinking down into a different part of that lost child. *But I love music!* Yeah, one would think playing music is better than being an addict of an actual substance. Well, I have news for you, being busy in this way was just another form of numbing the hurt, trauma, or whatever demons or feelings I was trying to suppress.

As for the men in my life. Hell, where do I start?! What story do you want first? My father? Nah, that's too easy.

I suffered some serious mental abuse and didn't recognize it as being such until a few years ago! Yup. You heard that right, people. All those years and never once did the recognition of mental abuse cross my mind. I saw such abuse being done to others, and I could point shit out, but for some reason, I didn't see the abuse happening to me. Or maybe I just didn't want to see it.

When you don't have a positive role model, you don't know what to expect. When you're surrounded by nothing but toxic relationships you have no idea how a woman, or any human being, should be treated. I thought, *as long as he doesn't touch me, I'll be okay.* That couldn't be further from the truth.

Mental abuse is just as bad as physical abuse. It tears you down from the inside out, slowly and painfully, to the point where you don't want to live anymore.

It was an early afternoon, and I was at work. I was arguing with my then-boyfriend. I don't even recall what we were arguing about, but it got to the point where I found an excuse to leave early for lunch. I couldn't walk out fast enough. I felt a warm feeling throughout my chest area and had blurred vision in my right eye, which were always the signs my blood pressure was rising. I rushed to my car, and as soon as I got in, I started screaming and crying uncontrollably, "WHY, WHY, WHY?!"

I pulled my phone out and called my best friend, but when she didn't answer the phone, I cried even harder. "I swear if someone doesn't answer their fucken phone, I'm going to drive off a cliff." I then tried my sister. She answered as I continued to cry, "Are you okay?!" she asked. "No! This fucken man, I swear. I keep telling him I'm at work, and he won't fucken stop!" After about ten minutes, she was able to calm me down. And this type of event was not uncommon.

Months later, I'm sitting in a mental health class which I decided to take to better assist my brother, who has mild mental deficiencies. We were reading about the symptoms of different personality disorders, and it hit me. *Holy crap! My boyfriend has a lot of these, and so did some of my exes!* My research started the next day. I read book after book and listened to different psychologists who commented on various mental illnesses and their differences. Wow! What an eye-opener. This spoke to me.

After seeking help, I learned I have C-PTSD (Complex Post Traumatic Stress Disorder). I could now work on myself. I learned how to manage my emotions when my buttons were pushed. This was when I became more aware of all the trauma I suffered. My approach, however, was not only to turn to western medicine but also to the practices of my ancestors—plant medicine.

A more holistic approach has not only helped my mental health but also put me back in touch with my spiritual side, which I suppressed for many years because of my Catholic upbringing. The practices of my ancestors were not approved by my religion, or by most religions for that matter. However, I do believe in a Higher Power, in The Great Spirit.

I'm far from perfect or completely healed, but I'm well on my journey and have learned a lot. I've tried many things; some have worked for me, and others haven't. I can tell you that there's no wrong or right path to healing. Some will insist that you *have* to change your mindset. Others will insist the answer is through knowing God, while others will start with either diet, exercise, or both. I say, follow your heart. Don't allow others to overextend their stay in your head. Ask for guidance and listen to your intuition as much as possible.

Learn to listen to your body and sit with the feeling. If you get that ugly gut sense that something is wrong, then maybe that thing (a particular healing modality) is not meant for you at that moment, even if it's worked for someone else. Not everyone is the same; therefore, the correct healing modalities won't be the same for all. Don't rush into your healing. When things are rushed, we tend to half-ass them, and sometimes, we don't get positive results.

Also, it's never too late to heal. It's never too late to start on your healing journey.

If you feel like a failure after starting your healing journey, take a break, then get back up once you think you're ready to try again. And if you fail again, do not give up on yourself. Keep going. Find what works for you.

For those who "don't have the time," where there's a will, there's a way. If you have time to cut your toenails, you have time to do some self-care because self-care leads to self-love, and self-love is self-care.

For those who say, "But I have kids, and they take up all my time," I say to you, have them practice self-love with you. Break that ugly cycle. Teach them young. They will likely not fall into the same patterns if they learn from you. Be the change!

I, for one, am very grateful for my spiritual journey. I have unlocked healing modalities practiced by my great-grandmother and my grandmothers before her. I have also discovered other gifts along the way, and I'm sure I will learn more as I heal and grow.

There are different ways to start showing up for self and relearning to love yourself. Here are just a few suggestions.

Remember who you are.

There are several ways to start the process of self-love.

1. Eating healthier: We have been conditioned to just eat. But how often do we really pay attention to what we put in our bodies and how much we consume? How much do we really need to eat for our bodies to obtain the nutrients it truly needs, and what are some healthier choices? I found that although organic food is a bit more expensive, I'm consuming less. Why? Because my body is getting the nutrients it needs. Therefore I'm eating less and less frequently.

2. Walking: So many of us are too busy to put in an hour a day of exercise. So don't. Instead, start with a ten-minute walk for two weeks at least three days a week, then increase the days as you see fit. As you move forward, you can increase the number of minutes per day. The toughest part, even for healers, is getting started.

3. Take care of your vessel. Vessel? What is this woman talking about!? I'm talking about your body. Our bodies are precious. Not only does it matter what we put into them and whether or not we practice preventative care, but it also matters what we put on our bodies and how aware we are of what we do.

   A. Do we drink enough water?

   B. What kind of body lotions or oils do we put on? Are they all natural?

   C. When possible, do we consume organic foods?

   D. Are we mindful of how we treat our bodies?

   E. Do we thank each of our body parts?

   F. Do we honor our body by taking care of who enters our temple or who we share our energy with?

THE PRACTICE

Honoring your being ritual:

Allow yourself at least two hours for this practice. If you have long hair, you might need more time. I prefer to do this at night but anytime is good.

Elements and First Steps:

- Towel
- Soap
- Body exfoliator (if desired)
- Bath salts
- Essential oil
- Candle (preferably white)
- Put your phone on airplane mode
- Create a playlist with relaxing music; nature sounds are good, too
- Body oil or lotion (for after the bath)
- Comfy PJs or clothes to wear after
- Journal your experience, even if it's just one word

Run a hot bath. Throw in some bath salts and essential oils. I recommend lavender, eucalyptus, or a blend of both. As you mix all these things in the bath, be mindful of the water. Be grateful for what the water offers. "Thank you for your love and the way you will make me feel as I soak in you."

Light your candle and place it in a safe place. Turn off the lights and remove your clothes but while you do that, think about all the things you'll be washing away. All the things you want to release.

As you step in, think of the value of water. Think of how it's nourishing to your body. Imagine you are one with the water as you submerge yourself in it. "Thank you."

As you lay there, think of how the water feels as it hugs your naked body. Feel the love that this small part of Gaia shares with you. Mother Earth is holding you in her arms at this moment. You are her, and she is you—through water.

You can lay in the water as long as you feel the need. Once you get to the point where you will wash your body, be mindful of every step. As you scrub your arms, be thankful for them. They help you with everyday tasks. Be thankful for your legs; they carry you and help you get places.

Once you are ready to rinse, as you stand under the shower, be thankful for the clearing you have received.

As you dry yourself off, be grateful for your entire being. Then, as you apply your body oil or lotion, allow yourself to love every part of you. You can even say it out loud. "I love you arms, I love you legs, I love you face." This may seem silly at first, but this is just the beginning of all the things you will begin to be grateful for. Elements such as self-worth, acceptance of your vessel, love for your battle scars, if any, and as you take these steps, maybe you will also realize that you need to appreciate yourself more often.

Once you have gotten dressed, journal your experience. Even if you felt silly, write that down, "I felt silly." Be as authentic as you can be. Eventually, with time, this will get easier.

Self-love is not an easy place to reach for some, and it won't happen overnight, but when you do, boy, oh boy! Everyone around you notices the difference. You begin to attract more positive people in your life. Positive things start happening to you. You become a master at manifesting all the good that is meant for you. The best part is that you inspire others to have self-love.

I truly hope that this helps you in some way. May love reach your heart and fill you with joy.

Con Amor, (with love)

Milagros

Intuitive healer **Milagros Ruíz Bello Martínez Arámbula** comes from a lineage of healers. Her gifts started surfacing at the age of five, and later her visionary abilities returned when she decided to answer the call. Some consider her to be a jack-of-all-trades. She chooses to use this designation to her advantage.

A love of music has always played a huge role in her life, with over 25 years of experience. She often creates healing music during her meditations and curative ceremonies. As she puts it, "Mother Earth takes over and guides my voice and drum."

Overall, Milagros considers herself to be a perpetual student. Her great-grandmother practiced the ways of the Aztecs, and although her ancestor leaves big shoes to fill, Milagros is taking on the challenge wherever it may lead her.

In her spare time, she likes to create medicine bags and other crocheted items. She enjoys making custom drums and other ceremonial pieces as much as creating music. She connects with Pachamama by spending time in nature.

Her mission is to help people remember their true roots as she continues to learn about her own. She aspires to become increasingly educated about different cultures and healing modalities to better understand and relate to this planet's inhabitants.

"I am you, you are me, we are one."

SERVICES:

Healing modalities offered:

- Energetic clearings
- Oracle readings
- Shamanic works
- Sound & drum healing
- Meditations & Ceremonies

OTHER SERVICES:

- Gift discovery
- Spiritual integration, self-love guidance
- Shadow work
- Translations (English & Spanish)
- Bilingual voice overs

To connect and learn more about Milagros and her self-discovery, healing journey, and more services:

Website: www.milagrosmbs.com

Instagram: @conamormilagros @miss_milly_jay

Facebook Page: Con Amor, Milagros

Email: milagrosruizbello@gmail.com

"It's the mistakes that take us where we need to go and show us what we need to let go of."

~ Grandmother Rosa Bello

CHAPTER 17

LOVE IS NOT ENOUGH

BUILD BETTER BOUNDARIES

Katie Shanley, RYT, CHHC

MY STORY

It was the morning of December 28, 2016, and I'd been up most of the night before. I got myself ready to teach my weekly yoga class because, for the life of me, I couldn't figure out how to make a phone call saying, "Can't teach this morning; got assaulted last night."

So, I taught a yoga class the morning after my husband assaulted me.

My sister called me early and her shocked voice quickly turned into crying as I recounted the details of the night before.

"What happened?! We just had Christmas with you guys. I don't understand. I'm *so* sorry this happened. Are you okay?"

"Yeah, I think I am in shock. But, I should get ready to teach my class."

Cold water to the face, a quick tea bag compress on each eye, a little concealer on my face scratches, and I was out the door. Zero sleep and a lot of adrenaline mixed together in a way that somehow was fairly balanced, all things considered. And hey, it wasn't as if doing some yoga and helping folks to feel better in their bodies and minds could make me feel *worse*. You know in the movies when a character doesn't let on that they've been hurt or bit by a zombie, but you, the viewer, know and are shouting it at the TV? *Katie! You got assaulted last night! Your husband broke your car window with a shovel, woman! You're not okay!*

But, in a way, I was okay. Earlier that month, I left the company I'd been with for the last four years. I didn't have a plan for what was next career-wise and now my marriage got the metaphorical guillotine. Yet, as I taught that class, I felt empowered. Teaching was, and is, an act of love. By teaching that morning I practiced vulnerability.

After class, I met up with my oldest friend, whom I've known since we were six years old, at the diner down the street from where I lived. An old-school mobile diner modernized with some hipster vibes. We scored a booth by the window on this cloudy day and ordered some much needed coffee fuel. I held the warm mug with both hands, occasionally pressing it up against my bruised sternum. The coffee created an interesting trifecta drug-like effect when it combined with my overtired adrenaline. We ordered pancakes.

"What happened last night after you left us? I was so scared by how he was acting and I've always feared something like this might happen with him. My mom was scared too. We should've driven him home or followed you and made you come back to my mom's house."

"You couldn't have known this would happen. I knew he was acting horribly and would be riddled with regret in the morning, but I never could have imagined *this.*"

"You don't seem too injured, thankfully. Are you okay?"

"I mean, no, but also yes. I'm *alive*. Very minor injuries."

After showing her my scratches from the glass and explaining that my chest felt a little bruised, but how I had gotten so lucky, I again told the story of the night before. Lily put down her utensils and I followed suit. She took both my hands in hers and looked at me in a way that melted away the barriers I had put up over the years. She looked directly into my soul. While we were nearly 30 years old, I saw us clearly at ten, laughing until we thought we would surely pee our pants. This was someone who knew me, despite the fact that I may have forgotten. My hands trembled along with the rest of my body, but I gave a gentle squeeze.

"Katie, I need you to promise me you will not get back with him this time. I can't lose you. I *need* you to hear me. You could have *died*. Imagine if there had been a gun in the house."

My eyes widened so intensely; I wasn't sure I would ever blink again. I took my hands back slowly and picked up my coffee, inhaling a big whiff. *Imagine.*

"I thought about that. It's weird, but I feel like he held back. Like, he hit me, but he didn't punch me. I was truly scared, but the police called it *attempted assault*. So, maybe it wasn't that bad? Cuts are mostly in and around my eyebrows." My voice trailed off as I looked out the window, mug perched beneath my lips, taking pleasure in a moment of people watching. Outside it was dark, cold, and damp.

"You can't make any excuses for him. Please, promise me. Please. I love you. I need you alive," she pleaded as a tear rolled down her face and I reached out one hand, ensuring I could continue to sip my unlimited refill coffee with the other.

The diner booth seemed to exist in a different dimension, where it was just the two of us floating in space, like a picture ripped out of a magazine. No other sound, no other voices. I knew that whatever I said back could not be meant simply to appease. This wasn't someone trying to control me or someone I needed to prove wrong. It didn't matter that she tried to save me, that she was against the wedding, that I had wanted to prove her wrong so badly. She just didn't know him like I did. *No, but she knows me. Why didn't I listen?*

The bitter truth that I couldn't change the past set in along with the caffeine sweats. At this moment, Lily needed me to not only tell her that I would keep myself safe, but also to truly understand what that entailed and to mean my words. With my clammy hand in hers, I could feel my adrenaline wavering. I wished I could fast forward past all of this. My eyes closed.

Snippets of the previous night flickered like light bursts. Metal crashing deafeningly into glass, echoing throughout my car. Glass raining over me, a blood-curdling, inhuman scream erupting out of me without my control. A trickle of blood that I mistook for a tear. But no tears. Still, no tears. Knocked to the floor, a knee on my chest making it hard to breathe. At nearly twice my size, he could have broken me. *Why did he hold back?* Why did the whole thing feel like a bizarre dance, somewhat familiar and somewhat improvised? My words pleaded for him to leave me alone, but I knew no matter how the night ended, it was over anyway.

We'd been married *two months* and they were the best two months of our four-year relationship. For our honeymoon, we went to Maine. We indulged in weed gummies, toured breweries, ate way too much food, and shopped at vintage and thrift stores. In the evenings we watched binge-worthy shows, the type that your husband pretends to hate. But, on your honeymoon, when you ungraciously have your period, he holds you and laughs with you at this silly show that you know he loves too. We had a 75-degree day in late October and biked around an island off the coast. It was here I made the decision that I'd leave my job before the holidays. The office was moving and the commute wasn't feasible. I was excited for a fresh start, to pursue teaching more yoga and maybe revisit my holistic health coaching certificate. I wasn't sure what was next, but my husband was supportive and believed in me. We were in love and life was good.

Now I am unemployed and single.

"Katie," Lily squeezed my hand, bringing me (somewhat) back to the present moment. I lifted my eyes, which at some point opened, and were staring down blankly at my cold, soggy pancakes. My eyelids were so heavy, it was more like doing an ocular bench press. I was fading but couldn't imagine sleep would come anytime soon. Through my dry and bloodshot eyes, I looked back into Lily's soul and took a deep breath.

"I understand that I cannot remain married to him after this experience. His actions caused me to fear for my life and there is no going back. I'll keep myself safe. I love you too. And I love me. I got so *lost.*"

My voice cracked on those last few words, but still no tears came. My words felt clear and concise. Perhaps almost slightly robotic.

"I know you did. But, I always believed you would find your way back. Only because you're okay, I feel like I can say that I am almost *glad* this happened. Otherwise, I'm not sure you would have ever gotten away."

Those words hung over me and I flicked at them in my mind as Lily spoke about how I should be careful not to give him an opening and avoid talking to him altogether. *Gotten away.* Had this man trapped me? Had the love I felt for him trapped me? Isn't love supposed to conquer all? In hindsight I would recall all the times and ways I cried out for help. I would berate myself for not leaving sooner. For taking him back after I ended it for a good reason. For knowing this relationship was wrong and still marrying him.

"How did a girl like you find yourself with a guy like that?" I cringed, a slightly sick feeling developing in my stomach as I recalled the police officer's words for the thousandth time. *A girl like me? How the hell am I going to handle a deluge of questions like that? What the fuck am I going to do with all the wedding gifts?* I took a few rejuvenating bites of pancakes, reveling in my love of real maple syrup and the comfort of this simple breakfast food.

"What are you going to do now? I wish I could stay with you."

"I wish you could too. Maybe it's the adrenaline, but I just want to dance. Is that weird? That's weird. Why would I want to dance right now? I just feel like I only want to do things that make me happy, like that's all I can handle doing, and that would make me happy."

"You deserve to be happy. Dance if you want to dance. I think you should also be around *real* friends or your family. Fuck anyone who doesn't have your best interest at heart. Maybe get out of this town for a while. Maybe even think about moving?"

Two days later, I went to a party with a good friend, made new friends, danced, laughed, and had an amazing time. Two months later, I went on vacation with my family—the last one I would ever take with my mom. Three months later, I went to India to get my 300-hour yoga teacher certification—it was here that I finally cried for the first time since the assault. Six months later, my divorce was finalized, and a week after that, I opened my first business, a beautiful yoga studio. Six hundred days later, I remarried—a man who is truly my best friend and was there for me in the thick of my trauma, always ready for a dance party. Five years later, in the midst of a global pandemic, I closed my yoga studio and we moved out of the town full of triggers.

Time moves quickly no matter what you do, so it was important that I let go of the desire to fast forward and just took my life day by day, consciously practicing inviting things and people into my life that made me happy. This did not go perfectly. There has been so much joy and laughter, but there has also been grief, loss, loneliness, doubt, pain, and fear. There's no light switch or magic cure. We're human and life's a journey. When I stopped trying to chase happiness and just did more things that brought me joy and spent more time with people I love, I realized that it's those choices which help create strong boundaries, not restrictions. It's a lot easier to love yourself when you're treating yourself well.

Love is both not enough and all we have at the same time. Loving someone is never wrong, even if the relationship turns out badly. But, love is not enough to hold a relationship together and we must let go of staying with someone because we're resisting change. Change has caused me grief and loss, and honestly, that makes it way less scary. Change, like death, is inevitable. The suffering is in fear and resistance. Even if we know it will surely cause pain or hurt; resisting change will almost always be worse because this is where regret is born. Think of change like getting braces. Sure, sometimes they hurt, cut up your mouth, food gets caught in them, and you might get made fun of for a bit, but your teeth look damn good when they come off, don't they?! Mmm, and so smooth! When we wait for or expect someone or something to fill us up, to make us whole, we give away the power and faith in ourselves that we need to stay grounded.

THE PRACTICE

Creating better boundaries doesn't have to be about setting limits. It can be about inviting more of what you love into your life—doing more of what makes you happy.

This practice is about getting out of our heads and into our bodies. It's about working through discomfort to bask in the glory on the other side. It's about getting in touch with our inner child, a.k.a. our inner weirdo, and loving the shit out of them. Poor boundaries aren't a lack of restrictions; they're living a restricted version of our own lives. When we lack boundaries we put ourselves in a box, we settle, and we struggle with regret, self-doubt, fear of change, and lack of motivation.

Strong boundaries are based on a solid foundation, self-love, and removing restrictions we place on ourselves, so that we may live as our fullest selves and reach our greatest potential. To build better boundaries, try asking yourself what you would like to add into your life versus what you should remove. Naturally, all the stuff that isn't serving us starts to melt away as we invite more goodness in; there simply isn't space for everything.

As we get in touch with our body-mind connection, we start to recognize what is no longer serving us and acknowledging it can help us to let it go. *Breathe in joy. Breathe out fear.*

STEP 1: DANCE PARTY

All right, first things first. It's solo dance party time. Select a tune that you know will get you moving. When I did this practice just now, I chose "Timber" by Pitbull ft. Ke$ha, but I recognize my shameless millennial taste might not be for everyone, so you choose your own jam.

Keep in mind this practice builds heat and is therefore energizing. Everyone is different, but I tend to like to factor in some time in between this practice and going to sleep.

Close the shades, close your door, maybe even lock it, throw headphones on if you'd like, and make it as private and comfortable as possible. Make sure you have clothes on that you can move in and hit play. Here's the funny thing, when you first start dancing you might feel that familiar hot-face rush of self-consciousness. I did. Close your eyes or look around at the privacy of your setting. Keep going through the discomfort. *Get big.* I'm talking booty poppin', roller coaster arm waving, shoulder shruggin', jumping up and down. You should be hot and sweaty when the song ends, or sooner. Take up space.

The key is to dance the entire time, so do consider this when choosing a song. Don't get weird on yourself and turn it off. Nope, that's cheating. This is not stupid or cheesy. I mean, maybe it's a little cheesy but cheese is delicious. *Commit* and notice how you come alive.

Make sure you're breathing as you get down with your bad self.

Note: If you want to do your dance party with a friend, family member, or partner, absolutely go for it! It can be a super bonding experience.

STEP 2: COOL DOWN AND REFLECT

Did you end up continuing your dance party once Spotify auto-cued up the next banger? Amazing. Me too. Now take a comfortable seat or lie down on the floor. Let your heart rate slow down as you take deep belly breaths. If you're someone who enjoys journaling, grab it, or a pen and paper just in case. If that's not your thing, it's fine to close your eyes and just notice.

Here are some journaling prompts. Feel free to modify or go rogue with your journaling process. Take what works for you and leave the rest behind:

- How do you feel (other than hot and sweaty)?

- What emotions came up for you when you were dancing?

- Was this practice challenging for you? Why or why not?

- How do you feel this practice of pushing past limitations (in this case, perhaps self-consciousness) could help you build better boundaries?

- Do you feel empowered?

- In your life off the dance floor, what might you like to invite more of into your life?

Katie Shanley RYT, HHC

Katie is a trauma-informed yoga teacher and holistic health coach who specializes in empowering women and men to feel safe within their own bodies and to build body-mind awareness, particularly following trauma and grief. In addition to yoga and coaching, she has studied many other modalities of healing, including aromatherapy, herbalism, Tarot, Reiki, Barre, yoga therapy, meditation, and Yoga Nidra. Katie believes her superpower to be her vulnerability.

She is a survivor of domestic violence and went on to become a certified domestic violence counselor and write about her experience, helping thousands of people better understand domestic violence. Katie lost her mother in 2018 to early-onset Alzheimer's and realized then just how uncomfortable people are talking about death. She believes in normalizing conversations around grief, trauma, abuse, or any other challenging topic as a means of healing.

Originally from Brooklyn, New York, Katie now lives in Vermont with her husband and their two rescue dogs. Together they run a shop specializing in vintage clothing and wellness products, including Katie's intuitive aromatherapy products. The shop, Moonwake, is a shared passion project honoring sustainability, self-expression through unique pieces of fashion, and healing.

Katie offers in-person yoga and coaching in central Vermont as well as virtually.

Prior to moving to Vermont, Katie owned and operated a yoga studio for four and a half years. She has led two 200-hour yoga teacher trainings, certifying around 20 teachers as well as led healing retreats in Puerto Rico and Tuscany.

Check out her website, join her mailing list, and follow her on Instagram to receive healing resources and stay in the know about upcoming trainings, retreats, and more!

Connect with Katie:

Website: www.katieshanley.com

Instagram: @kshanster

Live your wisdom.

"Love is both not enough and all we have at the same time."

~ Katie Shanley

CHAPTER 18

BETRAYAL
HEALING THROUGH JOURNALING

Rochel Marie Lawson, RN, AHP, CMS

"Forgive yourself for the blindness that put you in the path of those who betrayed you. They were a blessing in disguise for you."

~ Rochel Marie Lawson

There is nothing more heart-wrenching in life than the experience of betrayal. Betrayal is something that penetrates the core of your heart and squeezes the loving and trusting life out of it to the brink of total collapse. Betrayal unleashes a lack of trust and confidence, producing moral and psychological conflict within your relationships and your mind. That conflict activates anxiety and worry. It activates a part of insecurity within you that creates a disturbance that leads to unnecessary pain, torture, and suffering in the mind, body, and spirit.

The poisonous thing about betrayal is that it will seduce you into not trusting in your judgment, intuition, gut feelings, or what you see and perceive to be true. The act of the deception will interfere with your internal guidance system, and you will feel like you need a tune-up or to be returned to a balanced state, like when you take your car in to get a tune-up. The subtle imbalances in your mind and body begin to rage out of control like a fire raging out of control in the middle of summer. The result is the chaos in your life. Betrayal destroys relationships, careers, health and well-being, mental stability, wealth, and life.

Nothing is more damaging to the ego and the sense of self-worth, self-trust, and self-love than an act of betrayal. It is one of the most difficult experiences to overcome because it involves breaking trust, which is earned utilizing honesty. Betrayal represents dishonesty and has the power to create irreparable damage to all that it embarks its life, squeezing grip upon.

Is it possible that betrayal is more than deception—lesson in self-trust and self-love? Is it possible that betrayal has nothing to do with the perpetrator or deception and more with the one deceived? Is it possible that the act of betrayal occurs in our life to assist us with learning to understand that love and trust in oneself is the greatest gift we can give others? When we understand this important life lesson, we become untouchable by the selfish acts and deceit others may try to impose on us. We become brave, bold, and unstoppable.

MY STORY

By the age of four, I experienced acts of betrayal occurring around me, and although I did not know exactly what it was called, I knew it was not right. These sensations became important to me later in my life

Four short years later, I learned the meaning of betrayal as it was something I witnessed many times, watching the interactions of adults in my family, particularly my father. My first experience with betrayal was when I saw my father kiss another woman while he was still married to my mother.

As I watched him reach out and pull this woman close to him, embrace her chin with his hand as he pulled her close into his body to place his lips upon hers, I thought, *Dad is cheating on my mom—he's kissing another woman.*

As I continued watching him, I thought, *This does not feel right.* I felt a lump in my throat; my stomach felt like I had a big chunk of poop right in the middle of it; I felt a flutter in my chest and an odd hum around my head.

My first personal experience with betrayal came at the age of 16. It is something that sticks with me today. I can remember the details of it as if it had happened yesterday. It involved my best friend and her boyfriend.

My best friend's boyfriend made several passes at me even though he knew I was not interested. I warned him several times that I'd tell my best friend Denise if he didn't stop.

It didn't stop; instead, it intensified.

He came to my house one day unexpectedly. We were sitting in my backyard chatting, and he began pulling me close to him and telling me how much he wanted me and how he was attracted to me. As I pushed him away, he grabbed me, pushed me down on the ground, got on top of me, and started trying to take my pants off. I was yelling, kicking, scratching him, and pulling his hair. He was 6 feet 3 inches, and I was about 5 feet 6 inches.

Fortunately, the attack stopped, and I told him to leave, and he did. Whew, nothing happened.

I vowed to stay silent; however, I told my best friend, Denise, *"Girl, your man is not who or what you think he is. He has wandering eyes, hands, and lips. I suggest you open your eyes and pay attention to what is going on in front of you with your man and your friends. His friendliness towards us goes way beyond what I call friendship."*

She didn't believe me. As her best friend, I wanted her to know that I loved her and did not want her to invest in somebody that was not worth her time, effort, love, or the sacrifice.

She knew how much I valued loyalty. She knew about what I witnessed with my dad on so many occasions and how I despised betrayal.

She confronted him; he lied and said I was coming on to him, and of course, she believed him.

She started spreading lies about me, saying I was "easy," a whore, cheater, and liar, and began sharing secrets I shared with her with everyone who knew both of us.

I confronted her, and it did not end well. We had a fistfight, and our friendship ended. I felt a deep sense of betrayal that turned to anger with a flame that raged inside my body for years.

Years later, I discovered she learned the truth about the incident with her former boyfriend and me because he did the same thing to her next best friend. She told a mutual friend of ours, Cherie, "I never knew how loyal Rochel Marie was until my best friend betrayed me like I betrayed Rochel Marie. I will always regret the day we stopped being friends. She was a 'ride or die' type of friend."

When I learned she said this, I became angry, and the fire within me raged as it did when our friendship ended years ago.

My second lesson with betrayal came shortly after the first lesson, and yes, it involved another male.

One of the girls I thought was a friend of mine cheated on me with my high school running back football player boyfriend. I confronted them both. She denied it, and he said nothing. I got that feeling I felt before when I was betrayed. My stomach felt like I had a big piece of poop in the middle of it, my chest had that flutter sensation, I felt that hum around my head, and I felt the energy of truth within me. Of course, the boyfriend denied the rumor; however, I knew it to be true. When my intuition speaks to me, it never lies.

We broke up, and I found out the rumor was true three days later. Betrayal had struck once again.

The pent-up fire of anger and rage was released within me once again. In my mind and heart, I felt I was not good enough.

The next major lesson with betrayal came about in the workplace. I had a colleague in a subordinate role to me. We became fast friends. I assisted her when she needed help with an assigned task. I covered for her when she made mistakes or left the job site to do God knows what. I thought she was my "ride or die" friend, but I was wrong.

I knew this gal was not loyal. During the time I associated with her, she betrayed every one of her friends. She was a hot mess; the writing was on the wall.

An older colleague of mine named Rosemary told me before she retired, "Do not trust her. She is a snake and is jealous of you. She is just waiting for the right moment to strike with her venom. She's not to be trusted. No matter what, never, ever let your guard down." I listened to those words; however, I didn't process the true meaning of those words until it was too late.

Intuitively I knew the truth. I felt it deep inside my gut; however, I neglected to pay attention to the feeling of truth within me. I failed to trust what I knew to be true versus what I wanted to be true. I was committing an act of self-betrayal instead of self-love.

She began sabotaging my work, telling my direct report and colleagues lies about me.

I began to experience extreme stress in my mental, physical and emotional body. I was always angry, the burning sensation in my gut increased in intensity, and I lacked mental focus and clarity. I became moody, anxious, and worried. I began to lose weight even though I had a healthy appetite. The people close to me noticed the radiance I once had on my face had disappeared. I was a mess because I was stressed and couldn't figure out what was happening or why.

Finally, during a meditation, all was revealed to me. I experienced feelings I had each time I was betrayed, the lump in my throat, that pit in my stomach, the flutter in my chest, and the hum around my head. However, something new appeared: a vision of the person betraying me. I was grief-stricken. I could not believe the person I thought was my friend, whom I confided in, was my hidden enemy, the betrayer.

This gal created havoc in my life and caused undue stress, which resulted in sleepless nights, lack of appetite, headaches, lack of focus, loss of weight, loss of money, loss of love for my job, anxiety, worry, negative energy strained relationships with my co-workers and my family.

My heart sank to my feet. My eyes filled with water from the intensity of the hurt and anger I felt inside. My blood began to boil, and my stomach tightened up as if it was getting ready to take a punch. My body trembled like a volcano getting ready to erupt. The heat in my body from the anger could not be contained, and I began to break out in a sweat.

This betrayal shook me to the core. I was filled with self-doubt, anger, and rage. I wanted to see her hurt and thought about having someone do physical harm to her.

I took notice of the theme of betrayal in my life and its effects on my body, mind, and spirit, and the words, *self-love* and *self-trust* began to appear in my thoughts.

*"I trusted you, but your words mean nothing because
your actions spoke the truth."*

~ Rochel Marie Lawson

And then the final act of betrayal occurred, and my life would never be the same again.

I let my guard down and experienced the ultimate of betrayals.

The game changer in my life.

This betrayal incident brought me to the core of heart-wrenching heartache and heartbreak. It was a complete mental, emotional, spiritual, and physical trauma, unlike any I had ever experienced. It broke me down to the lowest point I had ever been in my life.

When you put your faith, trust, and belief in someone, and they prove to be not worthy of the gifts you have bestowed upon them, it can leave you questioning everything you believe about true love and life.

When you discover that what appears to feel and be real is not a reality but a deception, it can be enough to make you question everything you think and believe about yourself.

I had clear visions when I meditated that I was being betrayed again and the faces of those involved in this betrayal. I was made to believe it was all in my head; however, I felt the truth in my body. I let go of the trust I had within me and placed that trust on something external to me that was not worthy to receive it.

I left everything I knew and gave up everything I valued for this person, only to discover that the fairytale dream was just a little girl's fantasy.

It was time for me to examine why this theme of betrayal stayed so prevalent in my life. I had a meeting of the minds during a meditation session, and I discovered that I was a catalyst for all the betrayal I had experienced.

The message revealed was that I did not love myself enough to see and experience the truth. I did not value my gifts and placed a higher value on others I believed to have gifts I desired. I desired to be valued; however, I had to start loving and valuing myself if I wanted others to.

I thought to love myself. I do love myself; however, what I discovered was I was not *in love* with myself, I did not value myself or the gifts that I had, and lastly, I denied seeing, feeling, and knowing the truth even when I knew it to be true. I felt all truths for myself in my body and saw them in my mind. Because of this, I had to repeat the lessons on betrayal until I understood to love and trust myself.

This last incident of betrayal was the worst experience of them all. And it was the best thing that happened in my life. This experience allowed me to discover the commonality as to why the theme of betrayal kept surfacing in my life and what I needed to do to circumvent it from happening again.

The beautiful thing about the lessons I've learned regarding betrayal is that I have learned to love myself. I understand that the deceptions I experienced were part of the plan to bring me to the point where I could love myself unconditionally without being dependent upon anything external. All was meant to occur to allow me to share the gift of learning to love and trust oneself unconditionally.

I get to share the gift of how to heal from a betrayal so that if betrayal ever presents itself to you on your path to bliss, you will have a tool to push through it so that you come out stronger on the other side.

"Every test in our life makes us bitter or better, every problem comes to break us or makes us. The choice is ours whether we become victim or victor."

~ Lorenzo Dozier, 31 Days to Live

THE PRACTICE

Betrayal has the power to rob you of all trust, faith, belief, and confidence in yourself and that you have in others.

Healing from betrayal through self-love becomes easy when you have the right tools to release and heal without judgment. The Divine desires for us to live a loving life. A life filled with love, joy, peace, well-being, happiness, and growth.

When you awaken to the idea that experiencing betrayal is part of the divine plan to assist you with unconditionally loving yourself as you travel down your path to bliss, it becomes a blessing in disguise.

THE THREE PAGE A DAY POWERFUL JOURNALING EXERCISE FOR HEALING

This practice is simple and powerful, allowing you to open to that special place within you where there is no judgment, criticism, or betrayal.

Before starting this exercise, repeat the following words seven times:

"I deeply and completely love and accept myself."

And now you are ready.

To begin, you will need a journal, composition book, or spiral notebook.

The process is simple. Every morning before you speak or engage with anyone, pull out your journal and write three pages daily. Allow whatever flows through your mind to flow onto the paper. Place no judgment on what is written. Just write.

The key is to be open to what is flowing out. You will be amazed at all the shit that has taken up residency in your mind without your permission.

You should do this every day with consistency; what you will notice is a theme to the things you have written. You will become conscious of the negative and disempowering beliefs preventing you from loving yourself for the beautiful, unique gift that you are to the world.

As these beliefs begin to spring up and you record them in your journal, try not to focus on them. Instead allow them to bubble up to the surface so you can acknowledge them and release them.

You will confront the disempowering beliefs head-on with faithful, loving, and empowering alternatives. This allows you to open the channels that have been closed for so long. You will gain insight about yourself you've buried deep inside you.

This is the perfect way to begin to rewire your brain and start the process of self-love.

Simple and very powerful.

There is one rule with this exercise: once you have written your three pages for the day, do not go back and read what you have written.

Please don't go back and read past journal entries. Let the past stay in the past. Once you have written it, the past has been released.

It would help if you did this exercise every morning without fail.

This simple little exercise is a life-changing exercise.

If you think the notion of healing through journaling by writing three pages daily in a notebook is poppycock, think again.

When I started doing this exercise, I realized so many things about myself that completely blew my mind; mostly having to do with faulty thoughts, giving my love to others before giving my love to myself, negative attitudes with revengeful thoughts. Connections with specific themes and patterns kept repeating themselves, highlighting disempowering belief systems that I picked up from others and carried like a badge of courage that wasn't mine to begin with.

I could analyze what I thought sucked in my life, such as the constant theme of betrayal, so I could uncover the things I was negating, which were loving and valuing myself for the gift to the world I am.

The first step in healing from betrayal with self-love is to make time for recovery, and you can begin this journey of healing through the three-page daily journaling exercise.

Wishing you a life filled with self-love and bliss.

Namaste,

Rochel Marie Lawson, RN, AHP, CMS

The Queen of Feeling Fabulous

Known as the Queen of Feeling Fabulous, **Rochel Marie Lawson** is a successful multiple business owner, registered nurse, ayurvedic health practitioner, dream lifestyle transformation facilitator, a multiple # 1 best selling author on Amazon, a 2-time international best-selling author, international speaker, and creator of The Brave, Bold & Unstoppable Women's Summits™. She is the owner of Blissful Living 4 U, which was created to bring wellness, wisdom, and wealth into the lives of individuals seeking a holistic path to living the life of their dreams.

A highly driven woman who was born to break barriers, she proves that when powered by purpose, women are unstoppable. She's built her storied life and career brick by brick, fighting fears, failures, and setbacks to have the success she's always known was hers to claim.

Today she personifies what it means to ascend above adversity while inspiring countless others to do the same.

Having honed her expertise for over three decades, her work is a testament to what it means to leave an undeniable mark on the world.

She inspires. She empowers. She unleashes.

Extraordinary at walking others through radical transformation, she is as relentless about her clients' success as she is her own. She is more than their coach; she's their champion.

Because she doesn't simply change lives—she expands them.

Rochel Marie's energy, insight, guidance, and enthusiasm have helped thousands of people improve their wellness, wisdom, and wealth by utilizing ancient, holistic principles that unlock the access for transformation to occur.

Her weekly podcast, The Blissful Living Podcast, has been going strong for eleven years. She has been quoted in the Huffington Post and featured on Fox, CBS, NBC, and several other prominent media publication outlets.

Connect with Rochel Marie Lawson:

Website:

www.blissfulliving4u.com

www.unstoppable-womens-summit.com

"Betrayal broke my heart. Learning to love and trust myself healed me internally and externally, and made me unstoppable!"

~ Rochel Marie Lawson

CHAPTER 19

THE ALCHEMY OF JOY
TRANSFORMING DARKNESS INTO LIGHT

Jessica Harvey, MA, MFT

MY STORY

"I'm sorry, you didn't get the position," he said to me. I stared at him unblinkingly as he continued explaining why they selected the man they chose to fill the role that I, for all intents and purposes, was already doing. I must admit I didn't hear everything he said, but I knew what would be coming a few minutes later. I was going to be *pissed*.

The long and short of the situation goes a little something like this: I was working for a large non-profit in the Bay Area in California for nearly four years, with nearly three on my current team. I worked my way up to lead clinician, but there were two problems. One is that the team grew exponentially under my current manager. The other was that, although I truly respected, admired, and enjoyed him as the leader of our team, there were certain tasks and projects he simply couldn't do without a clinical master's or a license—things I had.

We needed a second manager, and my teammates (and honestly, I personally) thought I was a shoo-in. I was on the team the longest. I performed half of the supervisor's tasks and barely saw any clients, so I could keep up with our team's administrative and managerial needs. So you can imagine my shock when he delivered the news that instead of promoting me, they'd be giving the role to *another* man with no license or master's. Nor did he have a day of experience on our team. I had a hard time digesting it. I was to stay on to support them both without the pay increase or title change. I was stunned.

What? Seriously? In San Francisco? In 2011? Doesn't this look bad for them? Am I really a mediocre employee? What did I do wrong? My rage and indignation grew. I received no feedback on what I could do differently. I felt ignored, dismissed, undervalued, and overlooked. For me, this would not stand.

Over the next few weeks I thought about my predicament from a few different angles. Staying was not an option, but I never thoughtfully considered what my actual options were. How could I *not know* what I wanted to do next with my life? I considered various agency positions, all with low pay and extremely challenging circumstances that made it difficult for clients or clinicians to be successful. The immediate opportunities I found were underwhelming to say the least.

I knew I had to leave, and my patience and self-worth at my job were rapidly draining, so I quit. I quit with no backup plan. I *had* to make something work, but what? I began to let myself think about what I would *like* to do. I was aware of what I *needed* to do (make money to live), but could I enjoy it as well?

I needed my internal values and feelings to match my external life and experiences. This is one of the tenets of creating joy. If I wanted to feel valued, I needed to find a way to make that a reality. If I wanted to work with highly motivated clients, I needed to figure out how to find them.

I began reframing the situation. *I have a clean slate now—what can I do with it? What did I not like about my old agency and position that was freeing to let go of?* While I had always thought about starting my own practice, it suddenly seemed daunting. I never seriously considered making that move while I was comfortable in my old position and workplace community. This is one way that "comfortable" can work against us.

Enter an old colleague of mine from a southern California internship. While a mere one year ahead of me, she was quietly building a psychotherapy *empire.* "Why not now?" she asked me. "What would you rather be doing? Would you like to get comfortable with another job that drains you in a system where you see little change?" I had to admit she had some fair points. She empowered me with some concrete first steps, and the prospect of something better felt a little more achievable. Could I possibly design a way to live and work every day that brought me joy?

I decided to give it a go—and it was not easy. I was still angry at my old management team for putting me in this situation and was incredibly lonely without my friends and work community around me every day. I ate little and slept a lot. I had textbook depression.

For those who have never suffered from depression, let me tell you that it *sucks*. I often say I wouldn't wish it on my worst enemy. The feelings of isolation were pervasive. *I am alone. No one else is experiencing this. I'm not doing anything with my days, and everyone else is busy at work.* Everything felt a little bleaker. I didn't enjoy the things I used to and had a hard time seeing what was next in life. *Where will I be in a year? Hell, what will I be doing in a week? What is going to happen to me?* I had some actionable steps, but as they say, depression can make doing the dishes feel like climbing a mountain. Imagine trying to start a new business under these circumstances! I knew I had to get professional support and increased personal connection in order to get me to a place in which I was able to pursue my joy.

Once I addressed the depression to a level in which I was more functional, I had to face that I had an incredible level of *discomfort.* I didn't know how to run a business, I was all on my own without any income, and I *had* to make it work. *Well, I might as well make this good,* I thought. So, I made it my job to learn. I took advantage of every free and cheap resource available to me in San Francisco and online. I learned the basics of accounting, taxes, marketing, website building, and office design. I talked to anyone who would talk to me, went to networking events, and got as much mentorship as I could find. For the first time, I possessed the knowledge to truly visualize what I wanted.

It took a few months, but I got my first office and website together. I placed business cards in the office neighborhood. I started getting calls. I didn't have a full-fledged business yet, but I was gaining momentum.

One day as I walked from my car to my office in Nob Hill, I realized I was happy—happy with where I was and where I was going, happy with what I created and the fact that I was working with clients who were so self-motivated that I could witness actual change. *This is what I have wanted to do.*

Was my joy-seeking over? Hell no! But I learned a few valuable lessons. One being that what had once felt like the end of my professional world ended up being the very thing that allowed me the space to create new circumstances more aligned with me. I could no longer imagine being a manager at an agency. I was living a more self-congruent life. That being said, I can say my anger motivated and propelled me forward. Anger has energy, and we can use it.

Another lesson, as cliché as it sounds, is that the greater the risk, the greater the reward. I could've gone to another company—smaller risk, smaller reward. I could've failed at starting my practice-bigger risk, bigger reward. When do we really go for it, go for what we want?

Having a private practice in an office I loved, with clients I loved to work with, would not be the end of my joy journey. But it did give me permission to let myself *want* things. What else brought me joy?

As a fairly extroverted person, I needed more interpersonal interaction. This could be challenging in a situation involving a lot of solitary work and little co-working or collaboration. I tried a few different offices until I was able to obtain my own space in a suite of clinicians I really connected with. I started a consultation group with colleagues who are still close friends today. I also loved a good party. I became the social chair for our San Francisco professional organization and spearheaded happy hours, holiday parties, and annual dinners. How could I get in all of the travel I loved to do? Well, being my own boss meant I could take off as much time as I wanted, set my own rates, and work as much or as little as I wanted to in order to make these trips happen. Fitting in some time for my love of animals? I was able to block off my schedule to volunteer at the SF SPCA once a week.

For many people, myself included, giving to others brings a powerful sense of joy. Of course, being a therapist is a great privilege and a fulfilling role to play in a person's life that brings me joy each day. But giving is also important in the community. For many in this field, there is a huge scarcity complex. Fears of not enough clients, money, office space, and other resources are pervasive. The outcome is that many psychotherapists are unwilling to give their time and energy to each other. I made it a point *not* to do that, to be generous with my time, insight, and energy. As others had helped me, I mentored, coached, and sent referrals to many less experienced therapists when they asked. This sense of community and looking out for each other still brings me joy today.

I cannot overstate the value of laughter. Laughter provides something healing and powerful for us both, physically and emotionally. I crack jokes often and laugh loudly in my life. And I strongly advocate for laughter in the therapy room. Of course, therapy can bring up a lot of pain, but hopefully it can bring up joy too. There is absolutely a space for this in therapeutic work, and most clients enjoy the balance it brings (obviously, you must be able to "read the room" and select your timing and language wisely). Allowing my clients to show up with all sides of themselves empowers them to connect with their joy and not only their pain. I was unabashedly thrilled when one of my office mates said, "We always hear you and your clients in there giggling and cracking up!" I took it as quite a compliment.

To summarize, pain and discomfort can be motivators. Much like physical pain, emotional pain is there to let us know something isn't working and needs to be addressed. Focusing on what brings us happiness and joy may require a lot of work, or it may not. In this case, mine required months of hustle. That might not be true next time. And there will be a next time, because remaining connected to our joy and working through pain are issues that will come up again and again in life. Yes, it might feel risky or scary, but that's the place where the greatest joys in life are often born. And it's always important to obtain the professional, medical, and interpersonal support you need in order to be able to move towards your joy.

Allowing ourselves to have wants in addition to needs is something many people struggle with. But we are each deserving of joy and happiness. I work with my clients on this daily. They're not only their pain, but also their joy. We actively work on clearly identifying what is in their control (opportunity for joy) and what is not (need to grieve and/or practice acceptance), and most importantly, to act accordingly. The flip side of painful situations in life, which we will all have, is an opportunity for more joy. Take it.

THE PRACTICE

PULLING JOY OUT OF PAIN

This is a reflection and reframing activity that's great for journaling. It's not intended as a substitute for therapy or getting professional help for grief, trauma, or mental health diagnoses. Use this tool in a way that feels helpful to you!

- What is the event bringing you pain?

- What specific feelings are you experiencing? Is there anything you're grieving?

- Which parts of the situation are in your control and which elements must you accept? There are almost always some of each! Be clear and honest with yourself about which pieces fall into these categories.

- What internal values do you want reflected in your external life?

- Practice reframing the experience as an opportunity. What does this situation give you the space to do now? What negativity or undesirable experiences can you let go of now?

- What have you wanted more of in your life? What have you been daydreaming about? What do you enjoy? Are any goals or long-term dreams relevant to your current experience? Allow yourself to focus on wants rather than needs in this activity. This can inform ideas that identify your joy so you can follow it.

- What action steps are necessary? Very Important—there is no change without action. What steps can you take to start incorporating more joy now? Remember to look at your notes about things that are in your control.

- Periodic follow up: Revisit this exercise every few months. Are you growing in a direction that has brought more happiness to your life? Have you been able to let go of any pain/anger/resentment since the triggering event? Do any of these emotions still need to be processed? What are the next steps you can take to continue focusing on increasing and moving towards your joy?

 **Jessica Harvey** is a licensed marriage family therapist in California and Oregon, and a New York Times featured psychotherapist with 15+ years of experience working clinically with clients. The last 11 years have been in private practice serving high achieving professional adults who struggle with relationship issues, anxiety, communication, life transitions, self-development, and self-worth issues. She also specializes in grief over the loss of an animal family member.

Jessica values incorporating laughter and joy into her therapy sessions, along with teaching emotional processing techniques and helping clients develop concrete steps on their journey towards healing and success.

Jessica was born and raised in upstate New York and attended undergraduate school in New York City. She then moved to California for graduate school and has been a West Coaster ever since! Her practice was established and developed in San Francisco, Califonia, and further grew into Portland, Oregon. She now resides in San Diego, California, and runs her virtual practice seeing both California and Oregon clients.

In her free time Jessica enjoys spending time with those she is close with, traveling the world, seeing live music, participating in water sports, and loving animals.

Connect with Jessica:

Website: www.jessicaharveytherapy.com

Linkedin: www.linkedin.com/in/jessica-harvey-6077431b

Facebook: https://www.facebook.com/jessicaharveytherapy

"The more our inner worlds—thoughts, feelings, values, and priorities—align with our behaviors and choices in our external world, the more space we create for joy."

~ Jessica Harvey

CHAPTER 20

SPIRITUAL FORTITUDE
ACTIVATING THE SPIRITUAL WARRIOR WITHIN

Abbie Martin

MY STORY

All I could think about were my two toddlers, alone in the house. *Would they find me in the morning? Would they be traumatized for life? How would they even know to get help? What in the world had I been thinking to check the mail this late at night when I had just moved in and knew absolutely no one?*

I stood motionless in the front yard, deep in the shadows of the pitch-black night, listening to the pounding footsteps getting closer and closer. I melted into the inevitability that this was how it was going to end for me. Fear had led me here and fear was going to kill me. My dad's voice was in the back of my mind shouting, "Never stop running, but if you get caught, then fight!" My body refused to move and my brain was nothing less than hijacked. *The reality was that fear, the internal terrorist that it is, was going to get me before the murderer did.*

My heart legitimately stopped beating as I felt hot sticky breath hit my ear, trembling as my hair was blown onto my face with their forceful exhalation. As quickly as I felt the heat of the breath, it was gone. I heard the retreating gallop and saw the shimmering outline of a massive deer, now running away from me.

"Oh my God, oh my God, oh my God," I whispered over and over. I felt silly now, knowing it was a deer, but my body still felt like it was about to be murdered and chopped into itty bits. *Why in the world had I allowed myself to be convinced to move outside the city?* My fear quickly turned to anger as I lashed out at myself, running through my list of regrettable decisions that led me here.

I'd like to tell you that was the end of the now aptly named "Terror Trip to the Mailbox," but it was just the beginning. While I may have been scared, I've always been more stubborn than a quitter. I pulled myself together and as I adapted to the low visibility, I gingerly walked along the driveway to avoid sharp rocks the rest of the way. I celebrated the small victory of having made it to the mailbox. *See, that wasn't so bad!* I stood in the street, closer to the one lone streetlight the neighborhood had and let myself enjoy the moment of feeling like I had accomplished something monumental. I grabbed the big stack of mail and as I shut the mailbox, I heard the dreaded sound of more pounding feet. They were different this time, definitely human and the pounding on the pavement was getting closer. I looked up the street and saw a silhouetted large man running purposefully towards me.

Like my worst nightmare, I tried to scream, but no sound came out. *Did he know I was there? I was right in his path, he had to see me. Was he coming to rob me? Rape and murder me?* He was on a mission and wasn't deviating. I dropped the mail, held on to the mailbox for dear life, shut my eyes, and waited again for the end to come. Instead, I felt the whoosh of him passing me by. I opened one eye and watched him turn into the next driveway and disappear into my neighbor's house. With the mail forgotten on the pavement, I ran as fast as I could for the safety of my home. I locked every door, closed the blinds, curled up on the floor of my kid's room, and gave into the ugly cry I had been choking on. Memories of myself in my fearless twenties were playing on a loop.

I used to be the fearless one in every single thing I did. While white water rafting, I volunteered on class five rapids to "ride the bull" on the front of the raft, only holding on with one hand to show off. I went to Hawaii alone simply for the adventure of it and learned how to fly a helicopter. I went skydiving not once, but twice. Now, I was alone in the world, with no friends or family nearby, and my whole identity was that of being a fearful overprotective mom of a son who was quite ill and could have an allergic reaction to something that would be the end of his life.

The next day as I gathered my damp mail off the driveway in the light of the morning sun, the next-door neighbor came out to greet me. She was very gentle with me as she said, "I wanted to check on you; that was my son last night. He's home on break and likes to run at night."

"Did he tell you I freaked out and thought he was trying to kill me?" I laughed.

"He mentioned you might have been holding on to the mailbox for dear life!" She relaxed as we laughed at that image. I was too proud to let on how mortified I was at my fearful overreaction.

As I walked back to the house I declared, "I am done with this version of myself. I refuse to let fear rule my life for one more moment." Whatever happened to me to bring me to this point, I was ready to unravel it. That meant taking inventory of all the things that now frightened me. My whole life I was told never to go out in the dark alone. I was reminded daily to lock every door all the time, including the car, and to remember that everyone I met was a potential predator. *Family values, check.* I started paying attention to what I watched and realized the local and evening news kept me in a constant state of terror. It was no wonder I didn't feel safe. The news validated everything I was taught to fear in life.

Truthfully, those were the easy things to look at. I reluctantly turned a discerning eye toward what I was voraciously consuming in my spiritual journey. I was a sponge as I consumed new-age teachings. I was all in on trying to understand the New Earth concept that was becoming quite popular. When I say all in, I mean I was *all* in. Every book, course, intuitive reading, or crystal I could get my hands on was purchased. The New Earth people were discussing ascension, going from 3D to 5D, warning that every structure was going to fall apart, and that in its wake would be a "New Earth." *But,* only those spiritually advanced or at a certain frequency would ascend.

In conjunction with ascending, I was devouring information about near-death experiences, the Pleiadians, the "Greys," and learning all about the Annunaki and how they were really the creators of humans. I was so gullible I thought this was new information just coming out. Hungry for some sort of confirmation of these fantastic claims, I was led down a path to more content that morphed into warnings of the dark forces on the planet. I was absolutely horrified to hear there was a conspiracy of the Illuminati or some larger-than-life group controlling the world. It didn't help that I was told by trusted people that they saw proof that the government was building concentration camps, that there would be a new world order soon, and that I needed to arm myself. It hadn't been intentional, but slowly I found I had stocked up on tons of canned food. I planted three vegetable and fruit gardens and multiple fruit trees in my acre plot of land. I even pulled all of my money out of my 401(k) and the stock market before it was supposed to crash. Bottom line, the spiritual world was scaring me with threats of not ascending and the conspiracy world was scaring me with the apocalypse and human trafficking. Does it shock anybody that I was petrified to check the mail in the dark?

As I looked at these things with a more rational lens, I was mortified at my naïveté and need to belong. I stood before the mirror and made a promise to myself, "I am no longer fearing that every choice means life or death for my son. I trust that this is his life experience and I can only do the best that I can do." The pressure released as I repeated this over and over again, easing my tension. I then went cold turkey and stopped watching the news and all the conspiracy theory videos. I wasn't conscious of how they helped me feel like I belonged to something, so I let myself grieve the loss.

I stopped locking my doors. Every single one of them. Not because I felt like I wouldn't get robbed, but because I wanted to disrupt the fear cycle it started for me. I checked the mail late at night for months, repeating to myself every night, "I am safe and protected." The deer and I crossed paths many evenings after that, but now it was like a sweet meet-and-greet versus a murderous rampage.

The first test came when a neighbor urgently came to warn me about a rash of break-ins in our area and she begged me, "I'm really worried for you and the boys. I really think you should consider locking everything down for their safety." The implication was clear, to be a good mom I needed to be frightened.

I stood at the threshold of my house again that night and considered my two choices. I could lock the car doors from there with my clicker and wait until the morning to check the mail. Or, I could step into the truth that I didn't want to live in fear of the what-ifs. I will never forget beaming like a lighthouse down to the mailbox, finally embodying the knowledge that my thoughts were creating my reality in real-time. I had zero control if my car was broken into or not. I could only control my experience around it. Living in fear that it was inevitable, versus the power of knowing I would be fine either way. It brought home the following three universal truths:

1. We all want to feel safe and that we belong—no exceptions.

2. Fear is an incredibly powerful motivator.

3. Spiritual fortitude takes effort and practice.

Thankfully, my trip down the serial killer deer and conspiracy fear-based rabbit hole was a tiny blip in my timeline, but that hasn't been the case for so many in the collective during these chaotic and truly divisive times. I still scroll social media today and get bombarded by the fear of the New World Order, our corrupt government, or the struggles of mystical portals ushering in new timelines or warnings about not bringing in enough light! I know I'm not the only one navigating these things, desperately wanting to be a discerning spiritual warrior in these crazy times. Had I not had that "Terror Trip to the Mailbox," well—I can't begin to imagine my reactions to them now.

It is worth discussing that scary things are possible. The love and light brigade of the new-age spiritual world did us no favors. I don't pretend that horrible things aren't happening in the world or deny that some of the twisted conspiracies might be true. I work hard to never lose sight that we're in a dualistic world that will always be reflecting positive/negative or light/dark choices. True power is in choosing how you will respond to what you're experiencing and your spiritual fortitude is the gift that you bring to the collective.

Imagine the difference if before reacting we said, "Whoa, I'm in my fear now. I will have to get back to this decision or situation when I've stepped out of fear." Which might frustrate others around you who are in their fear. You can't tell someone not to be in fear when they're immobilized. Had someone laughed at my fear as I waited to die that night, they'd only have traumatized me. The world needs spiritual warriors that come from a place of spiritual fortitude or love. The unflappable, unshakeable warriors of love who understand the truth that we are divine beings having a human experience and fear is merely an emotion meant to teach you—if you choose to be taught.

That also means being compassionate and understanding when you do get shaken up. My night of terror was well over 15 years ago, and I still have to work on the unflappable part. Those toddlers are almost adults now! Case in point, I found myself in a situation recently with a beloved family member who was incredibly frightened and concerned for me to be alone at the beach with impending storms while I waited on friends to join me. I found myself hunkered under an umbrella, petrified that I was alone in this impending doom. I whined, "I can't believe that I've been abandoned and all of my stuff will be soaked when the storm rolls in. I'm all alone in the world!" If you know me, then you know I'm a water baby, a self-proclaimed sea-witch. Spending the day alone on the beach is my actual happy place and yet here I was, legitimately cowering under an umbrella and fighting back tears. After a few hours, my body started to relax and I became acutely aware that it was actually quite a beautiful sunny day. I had taken on their fear and lost my own spiritual fortitude without being remotely conscious of it.

Unflappable doesn't mean never being afraid; it just means getting through the other side of the lesson a whole lot faster. With all the turmoil we have right now, we have the opportunity to practice, and then practice some more. It's my hope to provide you with this spiritual practice to help you tap into your spiritual fortitude so you can choose to be in your power and choose love in a world of chaos—over and over and over again.

THE PRACTICE

STEP 1

Step one is to seek clarity around what is going on when you're in a fearful or upset space. Make the space to address the situation and ask yourself the following three questions before you make any internal judgments or decisions:

1. Am I in imminent danger? If the answer is yes, remove yourself from the situation first. If the answer is no, move forward.

2. What is triggering my fear in this situation? Is it truly mine or someone else's?

3. What does this remind me of in my past or repeating patterns in my life?

STEP 2

Come into your sacred space for a ritual or meditation, setting the intention that only love may enter. Call on support from your divine team. I like to call in the elements of air, fire, water, earth, and my ancestors for this work, but this only works if you make it yours.

Focus on your breath for one full minute. Breathing in for four, holding for four, and releasing for four.

Set the intention to connect to the earth, connect to your Divine Source with the help of your divine team, and then come into your heart space. Your heart space is where you receive and perceive the world around you.

Invite your guardian angel who protects you always, to step forward. Your guardian angel will have a special container or box and will place it before you. You're invited to release your irrational fears and worries into this box. Spend the time you need naming your situation, your fears and anxiousness, feeling it energetically releasing from every cell in your body and easing into this container.

Once you feel complete, feel back into your body and focus again for one full minute on your breathing. Let the energetic release be integrated into your physical body.

Sitting with your divine team and ancestors, ask the following questions:

- What is there for me to learn from this situation?
- How can I best choose love right now?
- What decision should be made from my power in this situation?
- What will it look like, feel like to be in my authentic power right now? Stay in the imaginative space envisioning and practicing the words of power you will speak.
- What, if any, action do I need to take?

When you feel complete, strong, and ready, thank your divine team, your ancestors, and your guardian angel for their support.

Focus your attention back on your breathing, and feel yourself come fully into your body. Trust you have left the fear, the anxiousness, the worry in a safe space.

You can carry this feeling, this strength with you forward, trusting you can return as many times as needed.

STEP 3

Repeat and then repeat again until you feel like you're standing on solid ground, fully embodied in your power. Spiritual warrior activated!

After many years of trying to keep her "woo-woo" under wraps, **Abbie Martin,** founder of Intuitive-Resources.com, decided that it was time to leave the corporate world, stop playing small, and follow her calling to help others with their soul expansion, healing, and manifesting journeys. Abbie is a spiritual alchemist, a Master Wiccan, an intuitive, and an energy healer with more than 20 years of expertise. Her mission in life is to provide her clients with magical tools to help them transform their lives and strengthen their connection to the Divine.

Connect with Abbie:

Website: www.Intuitive-Resources.com

Facebook: https://www.facebook.com/EmbraceYourWooWoo

Instagram: https://www.instagram.com/intuitive_resources/

LinkedIn www.linkedin.com/company/intuitive-resources-com

YouTube: https://bit.ly/3znkw6b

TikTok: Tiktok.com/@theintuitiveresources

"True power is in choosing how you will respond to what you're experiencing and your spiritual fortitude is the gift that you bring to the collective."

~ Abbie Martin

CHAPTER 21

SOUL COOK
TRANSFORMING EMPTINESS INTO NOURISHMENT

Dan Gorbunow

MY STORY

"Mom says, go away." He said it with a boy's softness, yet his words bristled through the screen door. My five-year-old son spoke through the sheer curtain. Behind him, in the shadows, his mother sat in the kitchen, feeding him with her distaste of me, coaching his words.

"We don't want you here. *Go away!*"

The screen door shut with a clatter and a click. Conversation over.

I was stunned; my whole body went numb. An owl screeched from the avocado tree.

Wow. Is this nightmare I am in really happening?

"Okay," I coughed the words out loud enough to get through the glass, "I will do as you say. Take care, son."

I forced a smile—a grim consolation, or perhaps compensation for the abject misery bubbling inside of me. At five years old, my son had the strength to send me away. I could respect him for that.

If you can do that to me, you will be able to do that to your mother when your time comes.

I began to break down inside as I walked farther down the driveway toward the steep mountain road. Life unreeling in slow motion, I shuffled, nearly paralyzed, under the Maui sun. Salt burned my eyes.

I left with nowhere to go, unsure of my next steps. Hope and courage I had arrived with on the island, not two weeks before, soured completely into a sad decoction of betrayal and shame.

I paused to wipe the sweat beading on my forehead. I was cooking from the heat inside me and the heat outside me.

Did I get all my stuff? Am I missing anything important? Everything.

Stalled on the edge of the driveway, facing the road winding down the grand mountain of *Haleakala,* sloping inevitably toward the turquoise sea, I was utterly lost.

Dude, how did you manage to so cleverly, brutally arrange your life to construct this disaster?

I choked tears as I slung my heavy bag over my shoulder and glanced one last time at the house beyond the avocado and acacia trees, and took the walk down from Kula.

This is just a bitter reminder of why things don't work out with some people.

Each breath was heavy, squeezing my heart. I sighed and clicked open the handle extension of my carry-on luggage, the same one I packed less than two weeks before to come there, to try again, to build the bridge of reunion.

Twisted remnants of palm leaves torn by gale winds in the gully alongside the hilly highway showed me what nature is capable of.

My shoulder stiffened with anticipation of the long haul. The small wheels of my luggage squeaked in complaint on the hot asphalt road as I marched.

"Go away!" "We don't want you here. *Go away!*"

Cars and trucks whizzed by anonymously as I plodded for several miles in deepening shadows, replaying the hurt record a hundred times.

I made it to Makawao, most of the way down. In a mad change of mood, I decided to return to the house to try again with my son.

I'll say anything, do anything. Apologize for anything. Beg for a chance to try again.

The inner voice of one of my elders slapped me to my senses.

Stop! There is no way I'm going to allow you to go back there and get beat up again. Leave them alone; get on with yourself.

I spun around in the street with my luggage, facing north to the beach, then spun again, looking up the mountain road.

I'm so lost right now. Curse that bright sun!

Seeking solace and shade, I stepped into a small mineral shop to buy a few moments pause, to find some purchase. I bought sage.

The clerk, a young tribal witch, looked at me and said,

"You can't have what you want until you stop grasping for it."

It was not easy to accept.

I started bawling and shuffled down the street, drunk with sadness, paying no attention to cars or people.

Goddammit! I have to, but I don't want to!

I don't want to let go! Not my son! This is killing me!

What am I going to do, my Creator?

I wept and worked my way down to the beach, to *Paia*, the North shore, to a familiar outcrop of rocks and crashing water on the beach that became my pop-up temple of grief and reconciliation. Nearby a sign read, *'Ho'okipa,'* meaning, *Welcome.*

Welcome the ancestors into ceremony, we are going into sacred space. Welcome the living. Welcome the four winds. Welcome the dead.

I am a walking dead man, ready to jump into the sea. Or fly home like a bird. Please end my suffering.

I took the path to the edge, where most tourists pause for a photo, then jumped the fraying salty guard rope, took the worn path to the sea, and climbed along the rocks and crags until I reached the tide pools.

The salt of my body poured through my eyes and met the salt of the sea carried on the wind, channeling down my face and chest, dropping into the vast ocean churning gently beneath me, rippling like a thousand waves of light and energy and life.

Go away; we don't want you here!

I yelled into the sea and spray crashing on the rocks.

This is how it's going to be then? The end of my half-baked fruitless plans? Misery and abandonment? Really? This is all you got for me?

A lone gull passed over me, watching me. I looked up, and my eyes caught a faint rainbow over the sun.

Hungry? You waiting for me to drop something?

Ditching my shoes and socks, I went into the sea. Rippling, vibrating cold water of the tide pool rolled around my feet; my sore toes dug into the sand for a long time. I peered out as far as I could see.

Looking out at the patterns of the sea, I remembered a story of how the indigenous Hawaiians and other South Pacific natives developed an uncanny ability to detect ocean currents and weather by looking at the patterns and colors. There were a thousand names for change, flow, and feeling.

All I see is grief and hurt raging in the deep.

If I go to you now, will you welcome me, ancestors? Will I be honored, or arrive in shame and defeat?

Death is too easy!

I dropped the heavy canvas bag off my shoulders, set the luggage down, and opened my palms to face the long breezes and crashing waves from the north shore.

Holy one, I just need a path out of my despair and uncertainty. Help me!

I took a breath and let go. And another. And another, with each crashing wave, until my spirit began to return.

I took

A

Breath

And

Let

Go.

I must let you go, my son, for now! I am not leaving you. In my heart, you are always there! I am being ripped apart, so I must stop grasping for you!

My only companions at that moment were *Pele* and the sea. These titans lifted my spirit back into myself, spooning honey into a cauldron. The aromatic grief simmered within me, seasoned by a hundred and thirteen beautiful things around me, stirred and whisked by a great dance of energy.

Another last burst of tears and another crash of waves upon the crags all mingled together.

Whose tears are saltier, yours or mine? We are one now, you and I; we are brothers.

I said prayers and thanked the ancestors as waves splashed in the sun on dark mossy crags kissed by the sea for thousands of years. I was just one more piece of the island in that moment.

I struggled to light sage. A wisp of smoke curled through my nose, entered my lungs, blew across my face, and got swept to sea in a swirl of currents.

Beauty all around me, I bless you! Help me, please, to leave this place in a good way! What now?

I felt pulled to the top of the island, the crown of Haleakala, above the clouds. I suddenly knew.

I will keep the smudge going and pray all the way to the top of the mountain. This will be my amends, an offering to my spirit, my lost boy, and those around him.

I will go up the mountain one last time, not to seek him, but to find myself.

I went up on foot, dragging my shit with me through neighborhoods and remote farms. Stopped and ate lemons fallen from a tree. I hitch-hiked several times. Lit and relit the smudge. Made my way, by and by, over several hours, to the top.

With each mile, the mood of despair and misery gave way to newness, more breath, and possibilities. My sore legs gave out, and I had to rest. I kept going until all other thoughts burned away, leaving only the desire to reach the summit. It burned in my chest and stomach until, somewhere along that road, my misery and angst evaporated in the sun.

I reached the peak and sat down, nearly breathless. I felt like a spirit floating in a bath of light and minerals. I wanted to lay down and collapse, but I kept myself sitting, spine straight, chin up. My eyes closed to shield the bright atmosphere.

The air on the crown has a strange quality to it. Sound echoes like tin through a canyon. The atmosphere and the sun are very bright, dense, and yet filled with subtle effects. Sitting, the last of the sage burning away, I breathed in the thin mountain air. Cold wind blew about, cooling me down.

Creator, I am here! I am cleansing my grief, holy ones. Ancient spirit of this place, see me and have pity on me.

Eyes half closed, I beheld a tall emanation, a shaft of light, an angelic being without human features, above me on the mountain, visiting through the rays. The being held aloft a thin bright brand of energy, a sword of light. It placed the light on my head, then touched my shoulders as if anointing me. Knighting me. The presence conveyed a message.

"Be at peace, my child; you are loved. Be light, be blessed. All you seek will be given."

Thank you!

The wind hummed through the rocks. I opened my eyes.

What just happened?

Strolling down the mountain through wisps of cloud vapor, serene, I made my way back down. The human activities below looked like tiny ants.

My body felt light with wonder and energy, and my appetite returned. It was getting late in the day.

I checked my phone and got a message from Sam, my son's ex-step-dad, who lived in the guest house behind my son's home. Sam and I had made peace early on – we shared a mutual problem, as his daughter was there in the house with my son. He said to call him.

"Hey Dan, I know you're going through some tough times. Come back to the house, stay with me in the guest house. Just please give them some space for a while until things cool down."

I have no better offer!

I accepted and made my way back, avoiding the main house. Later on, Sam returned from work with delicious grilled meat and fries. He was the kitchen manager for one of the top restaurants on Maui.

"If you want some work, my prep cook was supposed to stay on for another month but had to go back suddenly to the mainland. That means I need prep help right away. Do you know how to cook?"

Why, yes, I do! I replied. I was to start the next day. My life took a radical change, a new course.

What happened next was astounding. Dressed to meet my new boss and crew, I was lit with joy and confidence as I rolled into the five-star restaurant in the high-end mall lined with palm trees and a waterfall.

I left the host stand of the restaurant and went next door to the art gallery to borrow a pen so I could complete my application. I met Kevin, dark-skinned, suave, dressed like a million bucks, who said,

"You should be here! Not just here, like every tourist, but *be here,* on this island."

There's a saying; the island will welcome you in or kick you out.

I brought my application back to the restaurant and shook hands with the general manager. I was the new prep cook—done. I stopped by to say thanks to Kevin at the art gallery.

Kevin saw me and turned to Nina, his manager,

"Nina! Here's the new chef at _____!" Nina smiled and welcomed me to the desk.

"Dan! Sit down; you must be a famous chef! Sit down and tell us who you are."

She listened to my story and called in the cavalry. Not long after, Thereza came in, ready to shake things up. Thereza! She was a Moroccan art buyer, a talented old-school cook, and, it seemed, a local celebrity. Nina yelled to her across the gallery as she approached.

"Thereza, look who's here; it's Dan!"

"Hey, Dan the Man! I have something for you," Thereza declared with mischievous purpose as she strutted up to me. She wore a lot of gold on her rimmed glasses, necklace, and bracelets. She smiled through dark red rouge and a generous white set of pearls.

"Dan! I have a message for you!" she said playfully. Her Moroccan accent was charming; her authority unquestionable.

How did I get here? Who are these people? How do they know me? Shut up and listen!

She pointed up to heaven and declared,

"I have a message *from God* to *you.*"

Okay, I'm listening.

"*You* are going to be *fine.* You have nothing to worry about. Everything is happening for a reason. You better get ready for all the good things coming to you!"

Wow! I feel it!

I laughed and thanked her. They politely interrogated me at the gallery, sipping grape juice and eating fresh cake. I was invited to prepare food with Thereza at her condo at once. She and her husband were preparing food that evening for the master artist's birthday celebration the next day. They were convinced I was a top chef, and though I tried to explain how simple the matter was, they could not be unconvinced! I was invited to help her complete her task, to be the assistant chef. Thereza had other dinner parties coming up, too—could I please help that evening? Sure! We rode together in her BMW to her condo.

I was introduced to platinum-grade Moroccan saffron and the proper way to prep chicken. Thereza and her husband fed me as we prepared traditional Moroccan dishes. I hardly had time to recognize that I was completely in another zone, making food at a beautiful condo in Wailea into the late night, quite unaware that anything remotely horrible had just happened in my life.

I showed up the next morning at the restaurant and learned to prep squid, lobster manicotti, and hamburger cut from sirloin with the proper ratio of fat to meat. All daily tasks.

I stopped by the art gallery. More grape juice and wedding cake samples were served. The energy was buzzing. Nina invited me to stay the rest of the month in her family home in Pukalani so I could get to work easier.

"We have a big dinner party tonight; it's going to be a birthday to remember! You must be there; Thereza will want to show you off. You want to do massage there? We can drum up some business for you."

The party rocked. The artist knew a lot of people on the island. I was the debutante. I ate well.

I left Kula and my 'untouchable' status and was hurled light-speed into a new life. Nina, French-Haitian, *très élégante,* was a wedding cake designer, so I ate cake for breakfast and dinner, and sometimes in between. I slept on the couch and enjoyed being adopted into a well-oiled family machine.

I was lent a new Ford F150 truck to drive and never took the bus nor hitchhiked again.

I drove under a full moon to Maui Meadows, to a beautiful home built by Nina's brother Gabo, this family of Haitian ex-pats who had lived on Maui for decades. An Egyptian woman, whom I had just met at the birthday bash the night before, was making a dish of raw foods. She asked for my help to prepare food and serve. She waved and greeted me as I pulled up to the house. Nina, Thereza, and a half dozen other new friends were already there, opening wine bottles and hanging out.

"Hi, Dan! We're waiting for you!" she called out from the moonlit balcony as the smell of the sea, jasmine, hibiscus, and a thousand other tropical flowers and trees wafted through the silky night air, blowing through her chiffon dress and blue silk headdress and scarf.

I parked the truck and called out.

"I'll be right up!" I was about to grab the bag of fresh greens and herbs from the passenger seat when I stopped and looked up at the warm tropical moon, the balcony, and the trail of scarves returning into the house, well-lit with friends.

Where am I? How did I get to this magical place?

The night answered.

You followed the call of your spirit. You listened. You let go. You showed up to offer high quality, and high quality is welcoming you in.

THE PRACTICE

Today, years later, I am still asking the question,

How did I get to this magical place in my life?

The faces of my beloved family as I serve up food off the grill, or wake my kids for school to make breakfast, are magical moments. The smiles, love, and interpersonal nourishment are *my food,* what feeds me.

Food comes in many forms, and vitamins take on many guises. What does the traumatized spirit need to heal? What does the wounded boy or girl need to hear? And feel in their belly? Transformation, purification, and preparation, refinement of raw into refined, and shadow into consciousness. It takes time, patience, and dedication. Lots of dedication and effort. Cooking, transforming what grows out of the soil, or on the vine, or what feeds from the earth, is not only a metabolic but a spiritual activity.

The healer is also a cook. The cook is also an alchemist, a wizard, a witch, and a philosopher. When you assemble good ingredients together, in a thoughtful, loving manner, with a commitment to high quality, high vibrational healing process and presence, cleansed from toxins and shadow projections, magic happens. What is served up? A more satisfying life.

Have you ever experienced, or are you now experiencing, a point of urgent necessity to shift yourself out of destructive feelings and circumstances co-authored by your habits?

Are your unconscious tendencies leading you into losses and risks you are no longer willing to pay for or tolerate?

Do your relationships and your vision for yourself demand more, something from you that you have not yet manifested or clearly understood how to create?

I have been there too, and that's why I wrote this chapter, to help you along your path to realizing your power to create the life you seek. Perhaps your vision is unclear, or your talents are not 'online' in your life.

No worries!

That will all come in time as you prepare the soil of your subconscious for the seeds of brilliance you already have or that contain you.

Here's an exercise that works for me, a daily check-in with myself and my higher power. Try it daily for at least 20 days.

SOULCARE SELF-HELP EXERCISE: THE FOUR STATEMENTS

Follow this self-check-in daily to help you manifest your dreams and gather energy to create and manifest. This exercise will lay a foundation of self-awareness and inner alignment, essential for creative manifestation.

1. NAME AND PURPOSE. State your name out loud to the Universe, to Higher Power, the Divine. Stand up, recognize yourself. State your business and focus on what you're bringing in and calling in support for.

Example:

"I am Daniel, son of James, son of Anthony. Turtle Clan. Universe, Creator, be with me today and help me fulfill my vision, avoid conflict and making trouble for myself and others. I share my love, joy, and mission with All!"

2. ACCOUNTABILITY. What could use improvement? Own your share of the situation. Take positive action to mend and further your goals right now.

3. DESIRE. State clearly what you want, either in this situation or in this moment. For yourself. For others.

4. GRATITUDE. State out loud what you are grateful for, feed what you love.

When you connect with who you are, your abilities, your desire, and what you appreciate, you create a flow of energy within you to attract the energy and connections around you to fulfill your goals.

This is only a step in the journey of transformation. Make a new habit. Hire me, take my next live-online course, or join me in a retreat to learn the steps and engage in the process. You are worth it!

Life is magical!

Salut!

Dan Gorbunow is the award-winning author of *The Seven Secrets of Men's Spirituality*, Best-Selling Amazon author, Soulcare coach, and healer.

Are you ready to manifest more love, more satisfaction? Dan can help you access your alchemical potential, your cooking power. Not merely as a chef in the literal kitchen but as the transformative agent in your life. Spiritual culinary training, not only with pots and pans but with fireside fellowship and radical acts of healing and connection.

Join Dan in the next live in-person or online gathering to engage and purify, to feed and to get fed. Learn and share in an amazing group of co-creators as you access your own special talents, powers, and medicinal qualities in an upcoming course or retreat.

Visit www.WarriorVox.com

Soulcare Coaching page: to schedule your consultation and explore the ultimate coaching program, Nine Week Self-Mastery.

Courses page: for online Live-Virtual Group Courses and Home Self-Study options.

Odyssey Circles and Retreats page: for a calendar and description of live events, workshops, and trainings in incredible locations and venues around the world.

Publications page: to view Dan's award-winning and best-selling books and articles.

Dan has a degree in Traditional Chinese Medicine and has practiced holistic bodywork for 30 years. His lifelong immersion in comparative religion and mythology, Jungian psychology, indigenous ceremonies and ways of life, and martial arts have shaped Dan's life and mission. Dan enjoys cooking, travel, design, wildcrafting, dance, storytelling, ritual, and creating learning adventures for his family and clients.

"Love is the master chef that will cut you down in the field, prune your rough edges, rinse you in cold water until you're purified, chop you into mouth-sized pieces, season you with salt and bitter herbs, and cook you into your best version of yourself. Love has so prepared you in order to ensure what you offer will be delicious, nutritious, and hearty enough to feed the soul, yours and all whom you love."

~ Dan Gorbunow

CHAPTER 22

AWARENESS GIVES YOU A CHOICE
CHOOSE LOVE

Laura Di Franco

I know meeting the love warriors in this book has inspired you. I love that. That is part of the mission of this book and my company. We are over 500 authors strong now! I'm so proud of that!

Reading stories of people just like you should help you understand what's possible. We hope you're sitting there experiencing a light bulb moment about just what kind of life is waiting for you.

You can read books, learn tools, and feel inspired. You can hear words from a friend, mentor, or inspirational speaker and feel those goosebumps. You might get a download about the next best steps. All of these moments are amazing, and it's what you do with them, the aligned action you take, that's the catalyst for the change.

You will not feel clear, confident, or courageous first. You must act *with* the purpose-driven fears. You must take action *with* the feelings you have inside. When you're on the other side of that fear, the clarity, confidence, and courage will show up. If you wait to feel that way before you leap, you'll be waiting a long time, probably frozen.

With awareness you get a choice.

Making an aligned choice and taking action is the change. I hope you'll take some action after reading this book. I hope you'll choose love more often, especially the kind you shower on yourself. Choose a chapter to experience today. Carve out some time to read and practice the author's tool. Protect that time and take the action. If you have a question or need some guidance, be brave and reach out to the author of the chapter. They are generously there for you to answer your questions, continue the conversation, or support you.

These books are a starting point. They're meant to give you a powerful toolkit. They're also meant to give you a powerful healing community to immerse yourself in, reach out to, and get help from. You don't have to do this alone. You're not meant to.

There's healing as you read these words. There's healing as you practice the tools. There's more healing as you embark upon the inner work on your own. And there's even more healing when you have a coach or mentor to guide you.

Healing also happens within your community when you find a safe space to be your full-on self. What I hope you'll adopt as a regular question on this journey is: *What else is possible?*

On the most difficult days, I hope you'll take that deep, pelvic bowl breath, pause, ask yourself that important question, and then open yourself up to love.

If you're feeling moved by what one of our authors wrote, reach out to them! You can also join us in The Brave Healer Book Club where experts from many of our books are hanging out to help you! Find that here: https://www.facebook.com/groups/143744423674578

Be brave. Take some action as you close this book. Maybe there's something you haven't learned yet that could change everything!

THE MOST IMPORTANT THING

By Laura Di Franco

The most important thing in my life?

Waking to love, in every possible way

that helps me feel fiercely alive.

My ability to take that inspiration,

available at any moment,

even the impossible ones.

Being awake enough to choose love,

no matter what,

no matter where,

no matter who,

no matter how difficult,

no matter how ripped-open it leaves me. . .

. . . this is the most important thing.

To look at another with complete acceptance,

understanding,

and compassion.

No matter what they've said

or what they've done.

To forgive and move into love

letting that energy be what

infiltrates my heart.

I always have a choice,

so I must attempt to choose love,

not out of duty or obligation

to my parents or teachers

but to my soul.

A promise to take radical, complete care of myself. . .

. . . the same self who'll then

and only then,

have the other-worldly capacity

to give what's necessary to make a change.

The most important thing in my life

is a wild, crazy, big-ass, unexplainable love,

an unfiltered, out-of-the-box, bigger version

than I was originally taught,

a flavor created by me,

tasted only by those who dare

and delighted in by those

courageous enough

to step into another level of vibration

without truly knowing what's in store,

willing to risk it all,

willing to come crashing down,

and rise back up,

dripping in the sacred bath of the full moon

and ready to take on the world.

The most important thing in my life

is the warrior love

I was born to be.

With Warrior Love,

Laura

BECOME A BESTSELLING AUTHOR

Your words change the world when you're brave enough to share them. It's time to be brave.

Are you ready to become an author in one of our bestselling books? Or lead your own book project?

Reach out to speak to the Brave Healer Productions publishing team by emailing: support@LauraDiFranco.com

THE BRAVE HEALER WRITERS RETREAT

Join us in the powerful red rock vortexes of Sedona, Arizona, for The Brave Healer Writers Retreat, where you'll enjoy experiences crafted to inspire, transform, and educate the world-changing badass you are. Our focus is to help you share your brave words and work with the world in a bigger way.

https://lauradifranco.com/writersretreat/

You were born, so you're worthy. Your message matters. What if the thing you're still a little afraid to share is exactly what someone needs to hear to change (or even save) their life? It's time to be brave.